ALL-AMERICAN TRIVIA

S0-ASN-292

Who's Who
IN
America
We the People...

Publications International, Ltd.

Compiled and written by **Jill Oldham.**

Additional research and writing by **Alyssa Amedei** and **Sarah Gorr.**

Image credits: Art Explosion, JupiterImages, Shutterstock

Cover images: Thinkstock

Louis Weber, CEO
Publications International, Ltd.
7373 North Cicero Avenue
Lincolnwood, Illinois 60712

Permission is never granted for commercial purposes.

ISBN-13: 978-1-4508-5009-4
ISBN-10: 1-4508-5009-X

Manufactured in USA.

8 7 6 5 4 3 2 1

CONTENTS

★ ★ ★ ★ ★ ★ ★ ★ ★ ★ ★ ★ ★ ★ ★ ★ ★

ARTS AND LITERATURE

★ ★ ★ ★ ★ ★ ★ ★ ★ ★ ★

Things of beauty—words, photographs, paintings, architecture, and more—have been gifts through the years from American writers and artists. These creative folks have found their way into American history and into the questions and answers of this chapter.

Q. Who is known as the "father of the modern detective story"?

A. Edgar Allan Poe, one of the most influential American writers of the 19th century. Among his most famous works are "The Raven" (a poem published in 1845) and "The Tell-Tale Heart" (a short story, 1843). Poe has also been called the "Master of the Macabre."

Q. Who photographed *Monolith, the Face of Half Dome*—perhaps the most famous image in landscape photography history ?

A. Ansel Adams. The iconic photographer and environmental champion took this photo in Yosemite National Park in 1927. Ansel's crystalline, panoramic shots of America's national parks not only revolutionized the field of photography but also reshaped how the American public thought about its natural resources.

> ★ ★ ★ **FAST FACT** ★ ★ ★
>
> **American folk artist Grandma Moses appears in the Norman Rockwell painting *Christmas Homecoming*. The two artists were friends, and Rockwell painted her likeness at the far left edge of the painting.**

Q. Who are Nan Wood and Dr. B. H. McKeeby?

A. The models portrayed in painter Grant Wood's *American Gothic*. Nan was the artist's sister, and McKeeby his dentist. The famous portrait of a Midwestern farmer and his daughter in front of a white farmhouse has become a recognizable icon of Americana even to those who know little about art.

⭐ Born in Mississippi at the turn of the 20th century, Nobel Prize-winning novelist William Faulkner observed monumental changes in American race relations, and he chronicled them in stream-of-consciousness literature—including *As I Lay Dying* (1929), *The Sound and the Fury* (1930), and *Absalom, Absalom!* (1936)—that was as complex as the issue of race itself.

The "New Negroes"

★ ★ ★ ★ ★ ★ ★ ★ ★ ★ ★

They were called the "New Negroes": the brash, exuberant young voices of the Harlem Renaissance in the Roaring Twenties. Among the many writers, dramatists, musicians, artists, and sociologists in the New York neighborhood of Harlem who instigated an intellectual revolution were:

- Duke Ellington—jazz musician
- Langston Hughes—poet and writer, "The Negro Artist and the Racial Mountain"
- Zora Neale Hurston—writer, *Their Eyes Were Watching God*
- Alaine Locke—the first African American Rhodes scholar (who coined the phrase "New Negro")
- Claude McKay—writer, *Home to Harlem*
- Jean Toomer—writer, *Cane*

Q. Who wrote *Gone With the Wind?*

A. Margaret Mitchell. When the book was published in 1936, it sold a record-breaking 50,000 copies in one day and 1.5 million copies in the first year. More than 30 million copies of the novel have been sold worldwide, and it is estimated that 250,000 copies are still sold each year. Mitchell won the Pulitzer Prize and the National Book Award for the book. She died in 1949 after being struck by an off-duty cab driver as she was crossing the street in Atlanta.

Q. Who wrote *The Common Sense Book of Baby and Child Care?*

A. Benjamin Spock (1946). His views that parents should not commit to a rigid schedule in caring for infants, and especially should not be afraid to show affection, helped revolutionize childcare in America and beyond.

★ Painter Georgia O'Keeffe is known for her precise, geometric depictions of magnified flowers and leaves as well as the desert landscape of New Mexico. Among O'Keeffe's most iconic works are 1923's *Calla Lily Turned Away* and 1931's *Horse's Skull with Pink Rose.*

Q. Who are considered the leaders of the Beat Generation?

A. Jack Kerouac, Allen Ginsberg, and William S. Burroughs. The "Beat Generation" is the name given to a generation of poets, writers, artists, and activists during the 1940s and '50s. The name originated in 1948 when Jack Kerouac told a magazine interviewer that his generation was "beat, man." Kerouac later said *beat* was short for "beatific." Kerouac suffered through six years of rejections before his most famous novel, *On the Road*, was finally published in 1957. The thinly veiled autobiography recounts Kerouac's travels across the United States and Mexico in the late 1940s.

Q. Who was Samuel Langhorne Clemens?

A. Clemens, celebrated author and humorist, was better known by his pen name: Mark Twain (and not as well known by his other pen name, Thomas Jefferson Snodgrass). His most famous works are the novels *The Adventures of Tom Sawyer* (1876) and its sequel, *The Adventures of Huckleberry Finn* (1885).

★ It is largely thanks to lexicographer Noah Webster that Americans do not spell *color* or *humor* with a *u*. Webster's 1828 *American Dictionary of the English Language* contained 70,000 definitions—30,000 to 40,000 of which had never appeared in any earlier dictionary. It took Webster nearly 18 years to compile and complete his work. He was 70 years old when the dictionary was published.

Q. Walt Whitman was a trained journalist and poet whose prose-like style helped free poetry from the constraints of rhyme and meter. Which book was Whitman's primary contribution to American literature?

A. *Leaves of Grass*. First published in 1855, *Leaves of Grass* was Walt Whitman's lifelong obsession. He regularly added and changed the poems that appeared in the compilation and issued five different editions of the work before his death in 1892.

> "*I went to the woods because I wished to live deliberately, to front only the essential facts of life, and see if I could not learn what it had to teach, and not, when I came to die, discover that I had not lived.*"
>
> —Henry David Thoreau, *Walden; or, Life in the Woods*

TRUE OR FALSE Poet Emily Dickinson was at the center of a group of intellectuals who collaborated and shared their work in the mid-1800s.

ANSWER False. Dickinson lived a life of self-imposed social seclusion in her Amherst, Massachusetts, home, writing poetry that often questioned the nature of immortality and death. She died at her family home on May 15, 1886, at the age of 56, after spending her entire adult life in almost total isolation. When she died, only her family and an inner circle of close correspondents and visitors paid notice.

> ★★★ **FAST FACT** ★★★
>
> Writer F. Scott Fitzgerald (*The Great Gatsby*) was a distant cousin of Francis Scott Key, who composed the lyrics to "The Star-Spangled Banner." Fitzgerald's full name was Francis Scott Key Fitzgerald.

Q. Which American artist helped to forge the style of art known as "pop art" by creating bold paintings that resembled large comic strips?

A. Roy Lichtenstein. Many of his oversize paintings took on a commercial style and sometimes looked more like a newspaper ad than art. One of his most famous examples of pop art, *Whaam!*, depicts a jet fighter destroying an enemy with an air-to-air rocket, all in strict comic-strip style, at a size of $5\frac{1}{2}$ feet by 13 feet.

Q. Who painted *Arrangement in Gray and Black No.1*?

A. James Whistler. Although many people would recognize this painting when they see it, very few know its actual title. It is more commonly known by its unofficial title: *Whistler's Mother*. Whistler was born in Massachusetts but spent most of his career in Europe, painting and doing etchings in Paris and London. He also became known for his skill as an interior decorator before his death in 1903.

Q. Which famous novelist was known to many by the name "Papa"?

A. Ernest Hemingway, one of the most well-known and successful novelists of the 20th century. He won the Nobel Prize for Literature in 1954. Hemingway made his mark writing about war and using his wartime experiences as inspiration for his compelling novels, which include *A Farewell to Arms*, *For Whom the Bell Tolls*, and *To Have and Have Not*, among others.

★★★ **FAST FACT** ★★★

The word *nerd* comes from Dr. Seuss, who first used the term in his 1950 book *If I Ran the Zoo*. The prolific children's author's real name was Theodor Seuss Geisel.

"Imagination has brought mankind through the dark ages to its present state of civilization. Imagination led Columbus to discover America. Imagination led Franklin to discover electricity."
—L. Frank Baum, author of *The Wizard of Oz*

Q. Which famous poet spoke at the presidential inauguration of John F. Kennedy?

A. Robert Frost. Frost was America's most beloved poet in the 20th century. He began writing poetry in high school, but none of his work was published until 1912, when *A Boy's Will* was published in England.

"Drawing is still basically the same as it has been since prehistoric times. It brings together man and the world. It lives through magic."
—Keith Haring, American artist and social activist

Q. Which author's 1962 book *Silent Spring* detailed the horrific effects of pesticides and launched the environmentalism movement?

A. Rachel Carson. Carson introduced the concept of *bioaccumulation,* in which a particular organism may receive only a tiny amount of pesticide but the problem is compounded as the pesticide progresses up the food chain.

Q. Who designed the Guggenheim Museum in New York City?

A. Architect Frank Lloyd Wright, who focused on designing buildings in harmony with nature and their environment. Wright designed more than 1,000 structures and completed 500 works, including office buildings, churches, schools, skyscrapers, private residences, and museums. The American Institute of Architects called Wright "the greatest American architect of all time." The renowned modern-art museum opened in 1959.

Author, Author!

* * * * * * * * * * * *

Match these American novelists with their famous works:

1. Truman Capote   **A.** *To Kill a Mockingbird* (1960)

2. Tom Wolfe   **B.** *Call of the Wild* (1903)

3. Jack London   **C.** *Rabbit, Run* (1960)

4. Kurt Vonnegut   **D.** *Breakfast at Tiffany's* (1958)

5. Harper Lee   **E.** *The Naked and the Dead* (1948)

6. John Updike   **F.** *Fahrenheit 451* (1953)

7. Ray Bradbury   **G.** *The Right Stuff* (1979)

8. Norman Mailer   **H.** *Slaughterhouse-Five* (1969)

Answers: 1. D, 2. G, 3. B, 4. H, 5. A, 6. C, 7. F, 8. E

TRUE OR FALSE John Steinbeck's epic novel *The Grapes of Wrath* was based on a series of newspaper articles.

ANSWER True. The fictional account of the Joad family, forced from their Oklahoma farm by the Dust Bowl in the 1930s, was drawn from John Steinbeck's research for a 1936 series in *The San Francisco News* called "Harvest Gypsies."

Q. Which mid-20th-century American painter was the master of the "drip art" style of Abstract Expressionism painting?

A. Jackson Pollock. According to Willem de Kooning, a rival artist, "Jackson broke the ice" for Abstract Expressionism. Pollock would lay large canvases on the floor of his Long Island, New York, studio and pour or splash paint out of the can in an animated fashion. Some critics viewed his work as impulsive and untrained, but many regarded it as brilliant, dynamic art.

Q. Sylvia Plath published her only novel, *The Bell Jar*, using what pseudonym?

A. Victoria Lucas. The semi-autobiographical novel paralleled Plath's experiences with mental illness and electric shock therapy. The troubled writer and poet committed suicide on February 11, 1963, just two weeks after *The Bell Jar* was published.

Q. Which American "frontier" author received the Pulitzer Prize in 1922 and then became a recluse later in life?

A. Willa Cather. Cather, who wrote such classics as *O Pioneers!* and *My Antonia*, was openly attacked in the 1930s for her conservative politics. She dodged rumors about her suspected homosexuality, as she wore her hair short and often dressed in men's clothes. Discouraged by negative criticism of her work, Cather became reclusive and burned most of her letters, destroying many of the details of her celebrated life.

Q. Which American writer spoke at Bill Clinton's first presidential inauguration?

A. Maya Angelou. Best known for her prose, which includes the book *I Know Why the Caged Bird Sings*, Angelou is also a poet, playwright, editor, actor, director, and teacher. President Clinton commissioned her to write a poem for his 1993 inau-

★ ★ ★ **FAST FACT** ★ ★ ★

Anna Katharine Green wrote the first American detective novel, *The Leavenworth Case*, in 1878.

guration. The poem, "On the Pulse of Morning," garnered as much attention for Angelou's reading at the inaugural ceremony as for its content.

United States Poet Laureates
2000–2011
★ ★ ★ ★ ★ ★ ★ ★ ★ ★ ★ ★ ★

2000–01: Stanley Kunitz

2001–03: Billy Collins

2003–04: Louise Gluck

2004–06: Ted Kooser

2006–07: Donald Hall

2007–08: Charles Simic

2008–10: Kay Ryan

2010–11: W. S. Merwin

2011– : Philip Levine

TRUE OR FALSE Legendary playwright Tennessee Williams choked to death on a bottle cap.

ANSWER True. Tennessee Williams was a serious hypochondriac obsessed with his own sickness and death. He was shy and equally afraid of both failure and success. He died in 1983 as a result of choking on the cap of an eyedrop bottle, though drugs and alcohol may have been involved as well.

Q. Whose 1953 novel about censorship was censored itself?

A. Ray Bradbury. Reportedly, Bradbury wrote *Fahrenheit 451* in the basement of the UCLA library on a pay-by-the-hour typewriter. Ironically, the story examines censorship, but unbeknownst to Bradbury, his publisher released a censored edition in 1967, nixing all profanity so the book would be safe for distribution in schools. A school in Mississippi banned the book in 1999 for the use of the very words Bradbury insisted be put back into the book when it was reprinted.

ATHLETES

★ ★ ★ ★ ★ ★ ★ ★ ★ ★ ★ ★

From the baseball diamond to the gridiron, the track to the back nine, the ice to the hardwood, athletes have fashioned some of the most indelible moments in American history.

Q. Who boasted of being able to "float like a butterfly, sting like a bee"?

A. Muhammad Ali, *née* Cassius Marcellus Clay Jr. One of the greatest athletes of the 20th century, Ali was the first boxer to win three world heavyweight titles. He also created controversy by using his international fame to condemn war and racism at the peak of the turbulent 1960s. After boxing, Ali became a noted philanthropist.

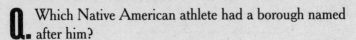

Q. Which Native American athlete had a borough named after him?

A. Jim Thorpe. Considered among the greatest American athletes of all time, Thorpe was an Olympic gold medalist, professional baseball player, pro football player, and the president of what would later become the NFL—and a Pennsylvania borough was renamed in his honor. In 1950 the Associated Press named Thorpe the "greatest American football player" and the "greatest overall male athlete." ABC's *Wide World of Sports* named him Athlete of the Century.

Q. Which baseball team was at the center of the scandal examined in the film *Eight Men Out*?

A. The Chicago White Sox. Eight members of the White Sox were banned from baseball for life for intentionally losing the 1919 World Series to the Cincinnati Reds. First baseman Chick Gandil was reputed to have orchestrated the plan, and although they were acquitted in a court of law, Gandil, Eddie Cicotte, Oscar "Happy" Felsch, "Shoeless" Joe Jackson, Fred McMullin, Charles "Swede" Risberg, George "Buck" Weaver, and Claude "Lefty" Williams were punished by baseball commissioner Kenesaw Mountain Landis. Many people believe that Shoeless Joe was unfairly punished, as there is no evidence he took part in the scheme.

Q. Which major-league athlete was at the center of "The Noble Experiment"?

A. Jackie Robinson. Robinson became a household name when he broke Major League Baseball's color barrier and became a popular civil rights role model. He was playing Negro League baseball when Branch Rickey, general manager of the Brooklyn Dodgers, gave him a major-league contract. After a year in the minors, Robinson was brought up to the Dodgers in 1947 in what has been called "The Noble Experiment."

> ★★★ **FAST FACT** ★★★
>
> The silhouette of a dribbling basketball player on the National Basketball Association's logo is an image of former Los Angeles Lakers great Jerry West.

"Take your victories, whatever they may be, cherish them, use them, but don't settle for them."
—Mia Hamm, National Soccer Hall of Famer and two-time FIFA World Player of the Year

★ The origins of NASCAR go back to the 1920s, when moonshine was transported illegally in an old Model T. Over the years, "whiskey mechanics" specialized in souping up V-8s, sawing cylinders to boost horsepower, and tweaking the rear suspension with heavy-duty springs and steel wedges to keep liquor bottles in place while driving on twisty mountain roads. The last NASCAR driver convicted of running moonshine was Buddy Arrington, who was nabbed peddling the homemade brew in the southern Virginia hills in 1969.

TRUE OR FALSE New York Yankees slugger Babe Ruth earned more money in 1930 than President Herbert Hoover.

ANSWER True. Ruth brought home a salary of $80,000; Hoover earned $75,000. When the fact that his salary exceded the president's was brought to his attention, the slugger reportedly said, "Why not? I had a better year than he did."

Q. Which prodigious 20th-century athlete was known as "the female Babe Ruth"?

A. Mildred Elle Didrikson "Babe" Zaharias. Her achievments in many sports, including basketball, track and field, and golf, established her as one of the greatest all-around athletes of the 20th century. She won Olympic gold in track and field, played baseball with the House of David team and pitched in major-league exhibition games, participated in a nationwide tour of billiards exhibitions, and won four major LPGA tournaments.

Q. Has a woman ever played professional basketball in the NBA?

A. No. Denise Long was selected by the San Francisco Warriors in 1969, but the NBA voided the selection. Lucy Harris became the first and only woman ever officially drafted by an NBA team when the New Orleans Jazz selected the Delta State star in 1977. However, she was not interested in playing in the NBA and refused to try out for the Jazz.

Q. Who did tennis player Billie Jean King defeat in the "Battle of the Sexes"?

A. Bobby Riggs. In 1973, the Houston Astrodome was the site of the famous tennis match. King defeated Riggs 6–4, 6–3, 6–3 in a match the London *Sunday Times* called "the drop shot and volley heard around the world." King remains an advocate for females in sports and women's equality.

> *"If you're in professional sports, buddy, and you don't care whether you win or lose, you are going to finish last. Because that's where nice guys finish, they finish last."*
> —Leo Durocher, Major League Baseball manager, *Nice Guys Finish Last*

Q. Who invented baseball?

A. According to historians, volunteer firefighter Alexander Cartwright (1820–92) is the inventor of America's national pastime. In 1845, Cartwright founded the Knickerbocker Base Ball Club and drafted a set of 20 specific rules that were intended to set baseball (or "town ball") apart from other bat-and-ball games such as rounders and cricket. These new rules included three strikes for an out and three outs per half inning.

★★★ **FAST FACT** ★★★
Gymnast Mary Lou Retton was the first woman to appear on a Wheaties box.

Q. Which former U.S. senator is also a Basketball Hall of Famer and Olympic gold medalist?

A. Bill Bradley. Prior to serving in the Senate, he won Olympic gold in 1964 and was a professional basketball player with the New York Knicks from 1967 to 1977. He served in the U.S. Senate from 1979 to 1996 and was elected to the Basketball Hall of Fame in 1982.

> ★★★ **FAST FACT** ★★★
>
> Chris Klug, a snowboarder who received a new liver in 2000, is the only athlete to compete in the Olympic Games after undergoing an organ transplant.

Q. Who wrote "Casey at the Bat," the classic baseball poem featuring "the Mudville nine"?

A. Ernest Thayer. The poem was first published in an 1888 issue of the *San Francisco Examiner,* under the pen name Phin.

Q. Which famed college football coach died in a plane crash in 1931?

A. Knute Rockne. Rocke coached the Notre Dame Fighting Irish from 1918 to 1930. At age 43, he finished the 1930 season with a 10–0 record and the national championship. On March 31, 1931, Rockne took off on a flight to Los Angeles; he was planning to serve as an adviser on a Hollywood movie about Notre Dame. One of his plane's wings broke en route, and the small craft dropped into a Kansas wheat field. He and the other four people aboard were killed.

Q. Which basketball coach was known as "The Wizard of Westwood" for building one of the greatest college sports dynasties ever?

A. John Wooden, head basketball coach for the UCLA Bruins from 1948 through 1975. He led the Bruins to ten NCAA championships over 27 years, including a streak of seven consecutive championships (1967–73).

Q. *The Pride of the Yankees* is the story of which New York Yankees superstar?

A. Lou Gehrig, the Yankees first baseman for 17 years. Despite playing in Babe Ruth's shadow, he was a powerful batter who dominated slugging for years. Gehrig died at age 37 from amyotrophic lateral sclerosis, a motor neuron disease that is now known as "Lou Gehrig's disease." *The Pride of the Yankees* paid tribute to Gehrig's life and immortalized his famous farewell speech at Yankee Stadium in 1939, during which he declared himself "the luckiest man on the face of the earth."

Q. Which college track phenomenon, known as the "Buckeye Bullet," earned a then-unprecedented four gold medals at the 1936 Olympic Games in Berlin?

A. Jesse Owens. The track star won gold medals in the 100m sprint, 200m sprint, long jump, and 4×100m relay. Although at the time his victories supposedly angered Hitler, who had expected the Olympics to showcase the "superiority" of the Aryan race, today a street near the Olympic Stadium in Berlin is named in his honor—Jesse-Owens-Alee.

Q. Which Pittsburgh Steelers football player, a cornerstone of the team's "Steel Curtain" defense, starred in what is considered one of the all-time-best Super Bowl commercials?

A. Mean Joe Greene. Even those who never watched a minute of football were familiar with the defensive tackle thanks to a 1979 Coca-Cola spot. Only a robot could refrain from smiling when Greene tossed his sweat-stained jersey to a kid in exchange for a bottle of Coke.

Q. Which sports announcer was known for the catchphrase "Holy cow"?

A. Harry Caray. Carey, who broadcast for the St. Louis Cardinals (1945–69), Oakland A's (1970), Chicago White Sox (1971–81), and Chicago Cubs (1982–97), supposedly talked his way into his first interview and was told by the owner of St. Louis's largest station, "Your voice has an exciting timbre." Caray went on to share that excitement with fans for more than four decades, most memorably at Wrigley Field. He was known for saying "Holy Cow!" and singing "Take Me Out to the Ball Game" during the seventh-inning stretch. His signature home run call was "It could be, it might be, it is!"

★ Vincent Edward "Bo" Jackson was the first athlete to be named an All-Star in two professional sports. Jackson was elected to Major League Baseball's All-Star team in 1989 as a member of the Kansas City Royals. The following year, he was selected for the NFL Pro Bowl as a running back with the Los Angeles Raiders.

Q. Who scored the winning goal for the U.S. men's Olympic hockey team in the "Miracle on Ice" game against the Soviets in the 1980 Olympics?

A. Mike Eruzione. Eruzione was also the team captain. His winning goal—one of the most played highlights in American sports—was voted the greatest highlight of all time by ESPN viewers in 2008.

Q. Who was named the greatest basketball player of all time by the National Basketball Association?

A. Michael Jordan. Jordan won six NBA championships with the Chicago Bulls. Other honors and accomplishments include the 1984–85 NBA Rookie of the Year award, two Olympic gold medals, six NBA Finals MVP awards, and five NBA MVP awards. He popularized the NBA and basketball around the world in the 1980s and '90s and was inducted into the NBA Hall of Fame in 2009.

Q. Who are considered "The Big Three" in professional golf, credited with popularizing the sport around the world?

A. Arnold Palmer, Jack Nicklaus, and Gary Player. An Associated Press poll proclaimed Palmer the "Athlete of the Decade" for the 1960s. *Sports Illustrated* named Nicklaus Individual Male Athlete of the Century. Player is the only modern golfer to win the British Open in three different decades.

"The spirit, the will to win, and the will to excel are the things that endure. These qualities are so much more important than the events that occur."
—Vince Lombardi, historic football coach and namesake of the NFL's Super Bowl trophy

TRUE OR FALSE American swimmer Mark Spitz holds the record for most gold medals won in a single Olympics.

ANSWER False. Spitz earned a record seven gold medals at the Summer Olympic Games in Munich in 1972, but swimmer Michael Phelps surpassed this total in 2008, winning eight Olympic gold medals at the Beijing Games. Equally astounding, Phelps set seven world records in the process.

Q. Who was the first male American gymnast to win the all-around title at the World Championships?

A. Paul Hamm. He took home the title in 2003, and he was also the first to win an Olympic all-around gold (2004).

Q. Who is the only person to be named United States Driver of the Year in three decades (1967, 1978, and 1984)?

A. Mario Andretti. Andretti is the only driver ever to win the Indianapolis 500, Daytona 500, and Formula One World Championship. He's also one of just two drivers to win races in Formula One, IndyCar, World Sportscar Championship, and NASCAR.

Q. Which Baseball Hall of Famer is the only player to play every inning of every game in a season, straight through the World Series?

A. Cal Ripken Jr., in 1983. Lou Gehrig's incredible record of 2,130 consecutive games seemed to be a feat that no one else could achieve ... until Cal Ripken came along, playing inning after inning, game after game, year after year. Ripken's appearance in every game for more than 13 seasons is especially monumental when you realize that during his streak more than 3,700 players spent time on the disabled list.

Q. Which baseball player was immortalized in Simon and Garfunkel's 1967 song "Mrs. Robinson"?

A. Joe DiMaggio. "Joltin' Joe" was introduced to a new generation of Americans in this song from the film *The Graduate*. The lyric "Where have you gone, Joe DiMaggio?" is an ode to lost innocence.

Eddie Arcaro, one of the greatest jockeys in horse-racing history, lost 250 races before he won his first. Ultimately, in a career spanning 1931 to 1961, Arcaro rode 4,779 winners.

Q. Who are the National Hockey League's "Golden Jet" and "Golden Brett"?

A. Brett Hull ("The Golden Brett") is by far the most prolific goal-scorer among American-born NHL players (741 goals). His nickname derived from his father's— fellow NHL Hall of Famer Bobby Hull ("The Golden Jet").

Q. Which professional snowboarder and skateboarder is nick-named "The Flying Tomato"?

A. Shaun White. The recognizable redhead won Olympic gold for the halfpipe in 2006 and 2010 and claimed gold in the Winter X Games five consecutive times in the superpipe— and scored the first perfect 100 in the men's snowboard super-pipe in Winter X Games history (2012).

> *"Don't look back. Something might be gaining on you."*
>
> —Satchel Paige, Hall of Fame baseball player

BUSINESS AND THE ECONOMY

★ ★ ★ ★ ★ ★ ★ ★ ★ ★ ★

The wizards of Wall Street and barons of business have certainly done their part to shape America. Stories of financiers, retailers, manufacturers, and pioneers of industry are all part of the American dream. Is your knowledge of business and the economy "on the money"?

Q. In 1882, two journalists set up an office in a Wall Street basement and started delivering financial news in hand-written bulletins. This operation evolved into *The Wall Street Journal.* Who were these reporters?

A. Charles Henry Dow and Edward D. Jones. They published their first Dow Jones Industrial Average, then a daily composite of 12 "smokestack" companies that produced coal, leather, cotton, and sugar, on May 26, 1896.

Q. Which successful retailer founded big-box retail giant Walmart?

A. Sam Walton. When the first Walmart opened in Rogers, Arkansas, in 1962, Walton stuck to several key principles: property owner-ship, no unions, low prices, low costs, and austerity.

> ★ ★ ★ **FAST FACT** ★ ★ ★
>
> Investor, entrepreneur, and philanthropist Warren Buffett began his illustrious career by collecting and selling lost golf balls. He also worked as a paperboy for the *Washington Post.*

Manufacturers had to let Walmart reps investigate their operations for ways to cut costs and give Walmart a better price. His method worked—and continues to work—because his customer base cares about lower prices above all (although the unions aren't happy). Walton also founded the Sam's Wholesale Club chain, in 1983.

Surfing the Web

★ ★ ★ ★ ★ ★ ★ ★ ★ ★ ★ ★

Match these Internet behemoths with their founders.

1. Amazon (1994)	**A.** Craig Newmark
2. eBay (1995)	**B.** Mark Zuckerberg
3. Yahoo! (1995)	**C.** Andrew Mason
4. Craigslist (1995)	**D.** Jeff Bezos
5. Google (1998)	**E.** Steve Chen, Chad Hurley & Jawed Karim
6. Napster (1998)	**F.** Pierre Omidyar
7. Facebook (2004)	**G.** Sergey Brin & Larry Page
8. YouTube (2005)	**H.** Jack Dorsey, Noah Glass, Evan Williams & Biz Stone
9. Twitter (2006)	**I.** Shawn Fanning & Sean Parker
10. Groupon (2008)	**J.** Jerry Yang & David Filo

Answers: 1. D; 2. F; 3. J; 4. A; 5. G; 6. I; 7. B; 8. E; 9. H; 10. C.

Q. Whose motto was "Get Big Fast"?

A. Jeff Bezos, founder of Amazon.com. Launched in 1995, the company grew rapidly, though all the while it continued to lose tremendous sums of money as Bezos opted for expansion over profit. After Amazon survived the dot-com bubble burst, it flourished. More than any other company, Amazon has made online shopping a way of life.

⭐ Early in 1929, John Jacob Raskob, chief executive of General Motors, published an article in *Ladies Home Journal* titled, "Everybody Ought to Be Rich." The article argued that if every American invested just $15 a week in common stocks they could all become rich. There was a major glitch in his plan even before the stock market crashed—the average American worker only earned about $17–$22 a week at the time. The article highlights the "psychology of prosperity" of the Roaring '20s, which was about to take a serious hit.

Q. Who was the first secretary of the U.S. Treasury?

A. Alexander Hamilton. Known as the great architect of America's financial system, Hamilton argued that the states should be subservient to a powerful federal government that could better formulate an economic policy for the benefit of all. He introduced controversial new taxes, paid off the country's war debts, and established a national bank.

"Economy is the method by which we prepare today to afford the improvements of tomorrow."
—President Calvin Coolidge

Q. Which American business tycoon funded nearly 3,000 public libraries around the world?

A. Andrew Carnegie. Over the course of his rags-to-riches life, the steel giant donated $350 million to cultural and educational institutions, scientific research, and the cause of peace. He is best known as the benefactor of public libraries, funding close to 3,000 of them around the world, the first in 1881 in his native Dunfermline, Scotland.

***

Q. Who served as the chairman of the United States Federal Reserve Board from 1987 to 2006?

A. Alan Greenspan. Six months after he became the chairman, Greenspan prevented the 1987 stock-market crash from becoming much worse. He directed the United States national monetary policy and was known for helping prevent inflation. However, Greenspan's economic policies may have contributed to the subprime mortgage crisis of 2007 that directly led to the recession of the late 2000s.

***

Q. Before cars made traveling to the store easy, much of the retail business in the United States was done through the mail. Who started the first major mail-order retail company?

A. Aaron Montgomery Ward. In 1872, Ward launched Montgomery Ward and began sending out Ward's "Wish Book," as it came to be known. Richard Warren Sears and Alvah Roebuck introduced their first catalog in 1896.

***

TRUE OR FALSE History's first recorded billionaire, John D. Rockefeller Sr., was a high school dropout.

ANSWER True. Two months before his high school graduation, Rockefeller dropped out to take business courses at Folsom Mercantile College. He founded the Standard Oil Company in 1870, made his billions before the company was broken up by the government for being a monopoly, and spent his last 40 years giving away his riches, primarily to causes related to health and education.

***

Q. In the 1920s, one American media magnate owned newspapers in every section of the United States. What was his name?

A. William Randolph Hearst. Hearst built the nation's largest newspaper chain with a blend of investigative reporting and sensationalism. In his heyday in 1935 he owned 28 major newspapers; 18 magazines; and several radio stations, movie companies, and news services.

⭐ In the 1910s, Henry Ford introduced a significant change in his factories that would forever alter the American workforce: the welfare capitalism program. Ford reduced his employees' workday from nine to eight hours and more than doubled their salaries from $2.34 to $5.00 per day. Though he was sharply criticized by Wall Street, Ford defended the move, claiming that not only did the $5.00 workday alleviate Ford's employee turnover problem, but it also allowed his workers to afford the cars they were building, thus boosting the economy.

Q. Two brothers developed a successful fast-food restaurant in San Bernardino, California. But when they sold the restaurant to Ray Kroc, they gave up the right to use their own name on a business. What was their last name?

A. McDonald. Richard and Maurice McDonald opened their fast-food shop shortly after World War II. Ray Kroc convinced them to franchise it, and in 1961 he bought them out completely.

TRUE OR FALSE Brothers John Harvey Kellogg and Will Keith "W. K." Kellogg founded the Kellogg Company.

ANSWER False. Although together the brothers invented corn flakes and founded the Sanitas Food Company in the late 19th century, they parted ways when Will wanted to add sugar to the flakes and John refused. In 1906, Will created his own company, the Battle Creek Toasted Corn Flake Company, which eventually became the Kellogg Company, and John formed the Battle Creek Food Company to develop more wholesome food products.

Q. Philip Danforth Armour, of Armour meat products fame, made his fortune gambling on hog futures. On what invention did Armour stake his future?

A. The refrigerated train car. The first refrigerated railroad car was built just after the Civil War. It kept meat products from spoiling and allowed farmers to expand the market for those products. Philip Armour sold hog futures for $40 a barrel, and he was able to fill orders with pork bought at only $18 a barrel.

Q. In the 1840s, "rich as Astor" was a common term for wealth. How did John Jacob Astor make his original fortune?

A. Fur trading. Astor, an immigrant from Waldorf, Germany, was one of the country's first self-made millionaires. He founded the American Fur Company in 1786, and by 1794 he controlled much of the beaver trade in the far West.

Q. Who is the "Ponzi scheme" named after?

A. Charles Ponzi. In 1919 and 1920, Ponzi convinced thousands of Bostonians to invest with his firm, sinking $15 million into International Postal Union coupons. It

★★★ **FAST FACT** ★★★

Time magazine called Ben Bernanke "the most powerful nerd on the planet." Bernanke, the chairman of the Federal Reserve, was *Time*'s Person of the Year in 2009.

was later revealed that there had never been any postal coupons. Instead, the man had used money from the later investors to pay earlier investors.

The eventual cofounder of Apple Computers and the brain behind the iPod, Steven Paul Jobs was adopted as an infant by Paul and Clara Jobs in February 1955. Jobs held an internship with Hewlett-Packard and did a stint at Atari, Inc., before he and Stephen Wozniak developed the first Apple computer. These days, the white cord of the iPod is ubiquitous, and Macintosh computers are synonymous with style and technical savvy. Interestingly, both Atari and Hewlett-Packard turned down Jobs and Wozniak when the duo offered the companies the opportunity to produce the Apple computer.

Q. A 1936 article in *Harper's Magazine* reported that wealthy Americans focused much of their hatred on one particular pair of people—and it wasn't dictators like Hitler and Mussolini, gangsters like John Dillinger and Al Capone, or radicals like Huey Long and Father Coughlin. Who was the target of so much emotion?

A. Franklin and Eleanor Roosevelt. According to the article, the "whole upper stratum of American society" reserved its most abusive language for the people who brought the New Deal to the nation.

TRUE OR FALSE The body of Teamsters Union president Jimmy Hoffa, who disappeared in 1975, has never been found.

ANSWER True. In 1975, labor leader Jimmy Hoffa disappeared near a Detroit-area restaurant. Hoffa, who was the president of the Teamsters Union during the 1950s and '60s, had strong connections to the Mafia, and several mobsters have claimed that he met a grisly end on their say-so. Although his body has never been found, authorities officially declared him dead on July 30, 1982. As recently as November 2006, the FBI dug up farmland in Michigan hoping to turn up a corpse. So far, no luck.

Q. Which investment manager shocked Wall Street, the hedge fund industry, and the world when his elaborate Ponzi scheme was exposed in 2008?

A. Bernie Madoff. He was arrested and charged with criminal securities fraud, accused of using his firm, Bernard L. Madoff Investment Securities LLC, to steal billions of dollars from his clients. U.S. prosecutors estimated that the size of the worldwide scheme came to $64.8 billion. Madoff pled guilty to 11 criminal charges, including wire fraud, mail fraud, and money laundering. In 2009, he was sentenced to 150 years in prison.

Q. Which fast-food entrepreneur introduced the drive-through window?

A. Dave Thomas. Thomas opened the first Wendy's (named for his daughter) in Columbus, Ohio, in 1969. In 1970, Thomas introduced the drive-through window, an innovation that allowed customers to purchase food without leaving their cars. The chain's commitment to customer service and quality products has remained unchanged throughout the years.

Q. Whose economic ideals were broadcast as a ten-part television series in 1980?

A. Milton Friedman. Friedman and his wife, Rose, advocated free-market principles with their television series and best-selling book *Free to Choose: A Personal Statement.* Friedman received the Nobel Memorial Prize in Economic Sciences in

1976 and was an economic adviser to Ronald Reagan. He and his wife advocated laissez-faire economic policies, arguing against state and government intervention.

Q. Who brought economics and pop culture to the best-seller list with his 2005 book *Freakonomics*?

A. Stephen Levitt. Levitt, a University of Chicago economist, won the John Bates Clark Medal in 2004, an award that recognizes the most influential economist under the age of 40 in America. Levitt wrote *Freakonomics* and its sequel, *Superfreakonomics*, with Stephen J. Dubner. Together, they argue that economics is the study of incentives.

Q. Who was one of the first economists to discuss topics like racial discrimination and crime along with economic policy?

A. Gary Becker. Becker argued that discrimination is costly to the discriminator. For example, when an employee refuses to hire someone due to the color of his or her skin, the employer loses the opportunity to hire a valuable employee. He discussed this theory, along with human capital, crime and punishment, and behavior in the lecture that won him the Nobel Memorial Prize in Economic Sciences in 1992.

★ *Capitalism: A Love Story*, a documentary by controversial filmmaker Michael Moore, is a study of the financial crisis of the late 2000s. Moore stated, "Democracy is not a spectator sport; it's a participatory event. If we don't participate in it, it ceases to be a democracy. So Obama will rise or fall based not so much on what he does but on what we do to support him."

CIVIL RIGHTS

★ ★ ★ ★ ★ ★ ★ ★ ★ ★ ★ ★ ★

In 1776, the Declaration of Independence observed that "all men are created equal." However, what looked good on paper took some time to become reality. The struggle for civil rights throughout American history has been the struggle to make that statement true for everyone regardless of race, religion, gender, or ability.

Q. Who was the first American woman to win a Nobel Prize?

A. Jane Addams. She pioneered social work in the United States, founded Chicago's Hull House, championed pacifism, and became the first American woman to win a Nobel Prize (1931). Addams campaigned for child labor laws, immigrant protection, factory inspections, women's rights, and general worker safety.

TRUE OR FALSE Ruby Bridges, the first African American child to integrate an all-white school in the South, had to eat lunches she brought from home because the cafeteria refused to serve her.

ANSWER False. Ruby had to bring her own lunch, but not because the cafeteria refused to serve her. Every day as Ruby walked to school, a woman would shout insults at her and threaten to poison her. In an effort to preserve her safety, U.S. marshals refused to let her eat any food aside from what she brought from home because they couldn't be sure the school's food was safe.

Q. Which well-known activist and author founded the American Civil Liberties Union (ACLU)?

A. Roger Baldwin. Baldwin founded the organization in 1920 to champion civil and constitutional rights through the due process of law. Also involved in founding the group were Helen Keller, Jane Addams, and future Supreme Court justice Felix Frankfurter. One of the ACLU's most famous early cases was the "Scopes Monkey Trial."

"My potential is more than can be expressed within the bounds of my race or ethnic identity."

—Arthur Ashe, social activist and the first African American ever selected to the United States Davis Cup team

---

Q. Poet and author Helen Hunt Jackson published a book, *A Century of Dishonor*, in 1881. She considered its subject so important that she paid to have copies delivered to every member of Congress. What was the subject of the book?

A. U.S. Native American policies. The release of *A Century of Dishonor* led to Jackson's appointment by the Department of the Interior the following year to investigate the condition of Native Americans in California. She offered a report in July 1883, but it made no impression on the government.

⭐ Betty Friedan is known as "the mother of the contemporary women's movement." In 1963, she exploded the myth of suburban women's domestic fulfillment with the publication of her book *The Feminine Mystique*, which described women's discontent and dissatisfaction. Friedan helped found the National Organization of Women (NOW) in 1966 and also cofounded the National Association for the Repeal of Abortion Laws (NARAL) in 1969.

Q. The first woman to run for president of the United States did so against Ulysses S. Grant in 1872, almost 50 years before women had the right to vote. Who was she?

A. Victoria Woodhull. Woodhull owned a successful stock-brokerage firm and was also interested in socialism and equal rights for women. The 1872 presidential candidate of the Equal Rights Party, she was in jail on election day, charged with sending allegedly obscene materials through the mail.

"I wish that Robert Kennedy and Martin Luther King Jr., President Johnson, President Kennedy, and others could witness what is happening in America. There [are] countless individuals that I wish could be on the Mall, on the steps of the Capitol and see what is happening in America."

—Congressman John L. Lewis, on the 2009 inauguration of President Barack Obama

---

Q. Who founded the National Farm Workers Association (NFWA), later known as United Farm Workers (UFW)?

A. Cesar Chavez and Dolores Huerta. Both sincere advocates of nonviolence, they worked tirelessly in their efforts to improve conditions for farm workers and their families. NFWA was founded in 1962.

⭐ On December 1, 1955, Rosa Parks, a 42-year-old African American woman, refused to yield her seat on a bus to a standing white passenger. Parks was arrested and found guilty, receiving a fine and a suspended sentence. The event sparked the 1955-56 Montgomery bus boycott, generally credited as the birth of the modern civil rights movement in the United States.

Q. Who was the publisher of *The North Star*, a weekly abolitionist newspaper?

A. Frederick Douglass. Having escaped slavery, Douglass devoted his life to advocating civil rights for all people. In 1845 Douglass published his memoir, *Narrative of the Life of Frederick Douglass, an American Slave.*

Q. Which former slave was famous for the phrase "Ain't I a woman"?

A. Sojourner Truth. Truth, who was born Isabella Baumfree in New York in 1797, escaped from slavery in 1826. After a life-changing religious experience, the former slave changed her name and began traveling the country advocating against slavery and for women's rights. In 1854, at the Ohio Woman's Rights Covention in Akron, Ohio, she gave her most famous speech, which contained the legendary phrase, "Ain't I a woman?"

⭐ The award-winning play and film *The Miracle Worker* are based on the true story of Helen Keller and Anne Sullivan. Keller's parents hired Anne Sullivan, a graduate of the Perkins School for the Blind, to teach Helen, who was deaf, blind, and mute, to communicate. Keller went on to spend her life working to improve conditions for the disabled, becoming a symbol of courage, dedication, and faith.

TRUE OR FALSE Harvey Milk, the first openly gay man to be elected to public office, was assassinated by Dan White because of his sexual orientation and pro-gay civil rights policies.

ANSWER False. Voting records, anecdotes, and newspaper coverage show that White actually supported Milk's agenda and even sought his friendship. The dispute seems to have been a falling out over land use and White's resignation. Regardless, Milk's

murder turned him into a martyr for the gay rights movement.
He was posthumously awarded the Presidential Medal of Freedom for his efforts in the lesbian, gay, bisexual, and transgender
(LGBT) civil rights movement.

Q. Whose legacy of peaceful protest for equality
is recognized with a national holiday in his
honor each January?

A. Dr. Martin Luther King Jr. A Baptist
minister known for masterful oratory and
nonviolent resistance, MLK was a leader of the
U.S. civil rights movement who fought legalized racial segregation and economic injustice from the mid-1950s until 1968,
when he was assassinated. Martin Luther King Jr. Day is celebrated every year on the third Monday of January.

In 1878, Elizabeth Cady Stanton authored a proposed constitutional amendment for woman's suffrage. The amendment was introduced into every session of Congress for the next 42 years, until the 19th Amendment was finally passed in 1920, granting women the right to vote—18 years after Stanton's death.

Q. Who were the Little Rock Nine?

A. A group of African American children selected to enroll in
Little Rock Central High School after segregation was ruled
unconstitutional. In 1957, Arkansas Governor Orval Faubus,
determined to maintain segregation in Little Rock schools, called
the National Guard to prevent African American students from
entering the high school. President Eisenhower, in turn, federalized the Arkansas National Guard and ordered them back to
their armories.

Q. This Boston schoolteacher began a crusade in 1842 to get better treatment for mentally ill patients, most of whom were housed in jails. What was this reformer's name?

A. Dorothea Dix. Dix wrote a letter to the Massachusetts legislature vividly describing the plight of the impoverished mentally ill. Later, as she campaigned to build a mental institution in New Jersey, Dix wrote that jailing the mentally ill made as much sense as jailing someone for contracting tuberculosis. Due to her efforts, by 1880 only 397 of 91,959 mentally ill persons—0.4 percent—were jailed.

> ★★★ **FAST FACT** ★★★
>
> Gloria Steinem is one of the most prominent faces of feminism in America. She is the cofounder of *Ms.* magazine, the Women's Action Alliance, and the National Women's Political Caucus.

> *"Women who seek to be equal with men lack ambition."*
> —Marilyn Monroe

Q. Which world-famous actress, dancer, and singer would fill an important role in the American civil rights movement despite living as an expatriate in France?

A. Josephine Baker. Baker never saw massive success in America the way she did in France, but that didn't stop her from taking an active part in the fight for U.S. civil rights. Not only did Baker refuse to perform for segregated audiences (forcing integration in some cases), but she worked with the NAACP and spoke at the March on Washington in 1963 alongside Martin Luther King Jr.

Q. Which outspoken advocate of LGBT issues formed an organization to reach out to teens who are being bullied because of their sexual orientation?

A. Dan Savage. In response to a rash of teen suicides in 2010, Savage created the It Gets Better Project by making an online video to tell young LGBT teens that life gets better and that suicide is not the solution. The project attracted widespread attention and now features hundreds of encouraging video messages from everyday people as well as celebrities and politicians.

Q. What organization did Carlos Montezuma found?

A. The Society of American Indians (SAI). In 1911, Montezuma helped found the Society in response to his negative experiences with the Bureau of Indian Affairs (BIA). He felt that Indian reservations were mismanaged, and he even called for the termination of the BIA. The SAI was the first Native American rights organization founded by Native Americans for Native Americans.

⭐ Bessie "Queen Bess" Coleman was the first female African American aviator. After earning her pilot's license in France in 1921, she returned to the United States and barnstormed at air shows around the country. She used her celebrity status to fight segregation.

TRUE OR FALSE Malcolm X was a proud supporter of the mainstream civil rights movement.

ANSWER False. Malcolm X was actually incredibly critical of the movement and believed that nonviolent defiance was not enough. He gave voice to the anger of the black community, urging that equality should come "by any means necessary." He argued that while he was not "anti-white," if whites were going to oppress blacks then he was against them. Though controversial, his beliefs are credited with giving foundation to both the Black Power Movement and the slogan "Black is beautiful."

Q. Who was Rodolfo "Corky" Gonzales?

A. Gonzales was a poet and political activist in the Chicano movement whose poem "Yo Soy Joaquín" ("I Am Joaquín") depicted what would come to be seen as the archetypal Chicano—a combination of American, Mexican, Indian, and Spanish identities. The poem, which ends on a message of hope and empowerment, would be used by the Chicano movement and frequently referenced or recited at rallies.

⭐ In 1869, Susan B. Anthony and Elizabeth Cady Stanton founded the National Woman Suffrage Association. That same year, Lucy Stone organized the less radical American Woman Suffrage Association. These two organizations joined forces in 1890 to form the National American Woman Suffrage Association (NAWSA).

Q. Who organized the 1969 Native American occupation of Alcatraz?

A. Richard Oakes. According to an 1868 treaty, the United States was supposed to return all retired, abandoned, or out-of-use federal land to the native people it had been

★★★ **FAST FACT** ★★★

Diagnosed with autism in 1950, a time when institutionalization was the norm, Temple Grandin is now considered a visionary leader in autism advocacy.

acquired from. Alcatraz had been abandoned since 1964, and Oakes, along with a number of Red Power activists, decided it qualified for reclamation. The protesters occupied the island for 19 months, leading to increased Native American activism as well as a change in governmental policy in support of Native American autonomy.

★ W.E.B. DuBois, champion of world peace and African American rights, was the first African American to earn a PhD from Harvard (1895). His 1903 *The Souls of Black Folk* was a seminal work in African American literature, and he was a founder of the Niagara Movement, a forerunner of the NAACP.

Q. Who was one of the first slaves to file a "freedom suit" and win in court with a ruling that slavery was illegal?

A. Elizabeth "Mumbet" Freeman. Mumbet was born into slavery around 1742. She and her sister Lizzy were acquired by Colonel John Ashley of Berkshire County, Massachusetts, when he married their owner's daughter. When Mrs. Ashley attempted to hit Lizzy with a heated shovel, Mumbet blocked the blow, injuring herself and losing the use of her arm. After hearing the Declaration of Independence spoken out loud, Mumbet sued for her freedom. *Brom and Bett v. Ashley* was decided in August 1781, and Mumbet became one of the first slaves to be granted her freedom, an act that informally ended slavery in Massachusetts.

THE CIVIL WAR ERA

★ ★ ★ ★ ★ ★ ★ ★ ★ ★ ★ ★

It was a period of American history that pitted "brother against brother." The Union army and the Confederate rebels stood toe-to-toe against each other, fighting to the death for their cause. The heroes, leaders, fighters, and historians of that era will not be forgotten.

Q. Which slave filed suit in 1846 in an effort to gain his freedom—a case that ultimately went all the way to the Supreme Court?

A. Dred Scott. The Supreme Court's 1857 Dred Scott decision ruled that Scott, as a slave and a black man, was not a U.S. citizen and therefore could not sue his owner, John Sandford. The decision inflamed sectional tensions between the North and the South.

Q. Which officer yelled to his men, "Damn the torpedoes! Full speed ahead"?

A. Admiral David G. Farragut. The Confederates had scattered torpedoes throughout Mobile Bay, and Admiral Farragut decided to take the heavily

> ★ ★ ★ **FAST FACT** ★ ★ ★
>
> President Lincoln originally asked General Robert E. Lee to command the Union army. Lee declined, of course, and resigned from the U.S. army to join the Confederate cause.

defended bay by force. After the Union ironclad *Tecumseh* struck a torpedo and sank, other captains hesitated with their ships, and Farragut shouted out his now-famous line.

Q. Which Confederate leader was known in the North as "the Brains of the Confederacy"?

A. Judah P. Benjamin. Benjamin was a close adviser to Confederate President Jefferson Davis and served in his cabinet as secretary of war (1861–62) and secretary of state (1862–65). As a U.S. senator, before the South seceded, he staunchly defended the legal basis for slavery.

"War is hell."
—Union General William Tecumseh Sherman

Q. Who was the Drummer Boy of Chickamauga?

A. Nine-year-old Johnny Clem. After being rejected from the Union army for being too young, he tagged along as a drummer for two years before he was allowed to enlist. In 1864, he was discharged at the age of 13. He later rejoined the army and remained in its service until 1915, retiring as a brigadier general. Clem is buried at Arlington Cemetery.

★ Mary Walker, doctor, writer, lecturer, and champion of women's rights, was the first female surgeon in the U.S. army and the only woman ever to be awarded the Congressional Medal of Honor (1865).

Q. With whom did rising political star Abraham Lincoln engage in a famed series of debates throughout Illinois in 1858?

A. Senator Stephen A. Douglas. Lincoln was considered the winner of the debates. Two years later, Douglas became the Democratic presidential nominee for president. However, Lincoln, the Republican candidate, defeated him again.

⭐ Grocery wholesaler Wilmer McLean hoped to get away from the war after his farmhouse fell under fire during the First Battle of Bull Run. An artillery shell even exploded in his fireplace after falling down his chimney! So McLean moved, but the war wouldn't be far behind. On April 9, 1865, it found him again when he lent his home in Appomattox Court House to Ulysses S. Grant and Robert E. Lee when they needed a place to discuss the end of the war.

TRUE OR FALSE The famous Confederate general Stonewall Jackson died in battle during the war.

ANSWER False. As Jackson and a small group of his men scouted out an upcoming path for his troops, a group of Confederate soldiers saw him and mistook him for a Yankee. The Confederates fired, wounding the general who had so often brought victory to the South. After surviving the amputation of his left arm, Jackson died of complications eight days after the incident, on May 10, 1863.

> *"In firing his gun, John Brown has merely told what time of day it is. It is high noon."*
>
> —William Lloyd Garrison, publisher of the abolitionist newspaper *The Liberator*

Q. During the Civil War, this former schoolteacher became known as the "angel of the battlefield." She later founded the American Red Cross. Who was this "angel"?

A. Clara Barton. Barton organized an agency to obtain and distribute supplies for wounded Civil War soldiers. Her work with the International Red Cross led her, in 1881, to establish the American National Red Cross.

Civil War Soldiers Who Became President of the United States

★ ★ ★ ★ ★ ★ ★ ★ ★ ★ ★ ★

- **Ulysses S. Grant (1869–77).** General Grant rose to prominence during the war and ran in the first presidential election that followed his victory at Appomattox.

- **Rutherford B. Hayes (1877–81).** Almost 40 at the start of the war, Hayes volunteered and was badly wounded in battle. He ended the war as a brevet major general.

- **James A. Garfield (1881).** Garfield fought in the Battle of Shiloh and, in 1862, personally led a charge that drove Confederate troops out of eastern Kentucky.

- **Chester A. Arthur (1881–85).** Arthur served as New York's quartermaster general and was nowhere near the front lines. He was ultimately awarded the rank of brigadier general.

- **Benjamin Harrison (1889–93).** Harrison raised a unit of volunteers in the Indiana infantry and served as their colonel. He was later promoted to general.

- **William McKinley (1897–1901).** McKinley served as a wagon driver in the Battle of Antietam. He was promoted to second lieutenant before the end of the war.

Grover Cleveland (1885-89; 1893-97) was the one president during the postwar years who didn't serve in the military. The sole supporter for his widowed mother, he hired a substitute to serve in his place.

Q. Walt Whitman's famous ode "O Captain! My Captain!" is about which American hero?

A. Abraham Lincoln. Whitman was fascinated by the war, and he left behind a catalog of colorful descriptions of its battles and political disputes. After the Union victory and Lincoln's assassination, Whitman wrote what is probably his most famous ode to his hero Lincoln.

Q. Who was the woman called Moses?

A. Harriet Tubman. An escaped slave, Tubman helped lead more than 300 slaves to freedom via the Underground Railroad between 1849 and 1860. She often used code phrases taken from the Old Testament to communicate to those awaiting rescue. "When the good ship Zion comes along ... be ready to step on board" was one favorite. Tubman also undertook a variety of wartime assignments for the Union army.

> ★★★ **FAST FACT** ★★★
>
> Two decades after leaving the White House, John Tyler joined the Confederacy and became the only U.S. president named a sworn enemy of the United States.

"I looked at my hands, to see if I was the same person now that I was free. There was such a glory over everything; the sun came through the trees, and over the fields, and I felt like I was in heaven."

—Harriet Tubman

Q. Who wrote *Nurse and Spy in the Union Army*?

A. Sarah Emma Edmonds. Edmonds posed as a man, Franklin Thomas, in order to serve in the Union army. As Thomas, she adopted several other disguises and infiltrated Confederate camps to obtain information for the Union. For the last part of the war she resumed her true identity and served as a nurse to soldiers in Washington, D.C.

Q. Whom did President Lincoln supposedly address as "the little woman who wrote the book that started this great war"?

A. Harriet Beecher Stowe. Stowe's famous antislavery novel *Uncle Tom's Cabin*, the story of a saintly black slave and the difficult life he and his fellow slaves endured, fanned the flames of hate across a divided nation. Radical abolitionists didn't think the book went far enough in denouncing slavery, while some Southerners condemned it as grossly exaggerated.

★ Major Henry Wirz, commander of the infamous Andersonville Prison in Georgia where 13,000 Union soldiers died in just over a year in 1864-65, was the only Confederate officer executed for war crimes. Unfortunately, it's not clear whether or not the responsibility for the deaths actually fell upon Wirz or whether it was even in his power to do anything about the terrible conditions at the prison.

Q. Who was Robert Smalls?

A. A slave in South Carolina, Smalls commandeered a Confederate ship loaded with armaments and delivered it to Union forces in Charleston Harbor. Having won freedom, Smalls joined the Union army and became the first black captain of a U.S. vessel.

Q. Which artist made a name for himself by creating Civil War illustrations and sketches for *Harper's Weekly* and other magazines?

A. Winslow Homer. The artist was one of several people granted "Special Artist" status and allowed to move around the war zone. His simple woodcut illustrations and sketches played a large part in shaping the public's perception of the war.

Q. Whose estate later became Arlington Cemetery?

A. Confederate General Robert E. Lee's estate was confiscated at the beginning of the war and used as a burial ground for Union soldiers. It was returned to the family in 1882 but was later sold back to the federal government, becoming Arlington National Cemetery.

> ★★★ **FAST FACT** ★★★
>
> General George Armstrong Custer disdained the clothing issued by the Union quartermaster and instead wore a uniform he had tailored. It was blue velvet, heavily trimmed with gold.

Q. Which Union general went on to write *Ben Hur*?

A. General Lew Wallace. Removed from field duty for a few years after his forces arrived too late to help in the first day of fighting at the Battle of Shiloh, Wallace acquitted himself at the Battle of Monocacy in 1864 by delaying a Confederate advance in Virginia and preventing the capture of Washington, D.C. Wallace later gained fame as the author of *Ben Hur*, published in 1880 and considered by many to be the most influential Christian book of the 19th century.

TRUE OR FALSE The first air corps was founded during the Civil War.

ANSWER True. Thaddeus Lowe, a self-taught scientist and aeronaut, used his skill as a hot-air balloon pilot to aid the Union. During the Peninsula Campaign of 1861–62, Lowe alerted General McClellan to the movements of rebel troops. It was the first time a commander was able to use aerial intelligence to track an enemy. In the end, Lowe's efforts proved a bit ahead of his time and his air corps was disbanded in 1863. Thaddeus Lowe, however, holds a special spot in the U.S. Military Intelligence Corps Hall of Fame.

A General by Any Other Name
★ ★ ★ ★ ★ ★ ★ ★ ★ ★ ★ ★

A string of increasingly embarrassing nicknames charted the Civil War career of Union General George McClellan:

- "Little Mac." The general was short in stature and had dark hair and penetrating eyes. His troops called him by this name affectionately.

- "The Young Napoleon." The general believed he was the savior of the Union and began treating civilian authorities with disrespect. Once he even refused to meet with President Lincoln when Lincoln called at his house.

- "Mac the Unready." General McClellan was notoriously overcautious. Confederate General Robert E. Lee took advantage of McClellan's timidity to win battles in which the Southerners were greatly outnumbered.

Q. Which Union general, later revered for his outstanding command of military strategy, originally left the army because he saw little future in it?

A. William Tecumseh Sherman. Though he got into West Point at the age of 16 and graduated near the top of his class, the military career that followed was lackluster and in 1853 Sherman left the army to become a banker. However, when the Civil War broke out, Sherman returned to service to fight for the Union. He slowly made a name for himself, and by the time he made his famous "march to the sea," he had become a high-profile figure.

Q. Ambrose Burnside, the inept and bumbling general who led the Union army to defeat at the Battle of the Crater in 1864, is also remembered for something of far less gravity. What is it?

A. His distinctive style of facial hair, now known as sideburns (derived from his last name).

Q. Whose images are carved into the granite face of Georgia's Stone Mountain?

A. The Confederate Memorial Carving shows three Confederate leaders of the Civil War: President Jefferson Davis and Generals Robert E. Lee and Stonewall Jackson. The carving, the largest bas-relief sculpture in the world, is larger than two football fields.

> ### *"Never be haughty to the humble or humble to the haughty."*
> **—Confederate President Jefferson Davis**

Q. When and where did Lieutenant James I. Waddell fire the last shots of the Civil War?

A. Surprisingly, Waddell's last shots were fired in the late summer of 1865 near Alaska, despite the fact that the war had been over since May. During the war, Waddell sailed his ship, the *Shenandoah*, for the Confederate army, terrorizing enemy ships in the North Pacific. His constant movement meant he didn't hear about the end of the war until August 2, at which point he surrendered to the British authorities who captured him.

ENTERTAINERS

★ ★ ★ ★ ★ ★ ★ ★ ★ ★ ★

This blockbuster chapter features the stars of stage and screen and proves that there really is no business like show business.

Q. Who has earned more Academy Awards and nominations than any other individual in history?

A. Walt Disney. Out of 59 Academy Award nominations, he has 32 wins—including a record four in one year—and he also received four honorary Oscars.

★ Writer/director Orson Welles shook up Hollywood and the country (not to mention the Hearst family) when he released the cinematic masterpiece *Citizen Kane* in 1941. Welles crafted the screenplay—featuring a somewhat fictionalized version of American newspaper magnate William Randolph Hearst—with Herman J. Mankiewicz.

Q. Which classic Hollywood starlet was able to place the Presidential Citizens Medal (the second-highest civilian award in the nation) next to her two Academy Awards and three Golden Globes?

A. Elizabeth Taylor. The star of great films such as *Who's Afraid of Virginia Woolf?* and *Butterfield 8*, Taylor would also come to be recognized for her tireless efforts in the fight against HIV and AIDS. She began speaking out at a time when it was very much taboo to do so and even co-founded the American Foundation for AIDS Research.

"I don't want to achieve immortality through my work. I want to achieve it through not dying."

—Woody Allen

Q. Who was known as the "Man of a Thousand Voices"?

A. Mel Blanc. Blanc gave voice to many of the Looney Tunes characters, including Bugs Bunny, Daffy Duck, Tweety Bird, Barney Rubble, and hundreds of others. His career spanned more than 50 years and included voicework in radio, TV, film, and records.

⭐ At the tender age of four, a freckle-faced boy with a toothy grin began a film career that would last several decades. America would soon come to recognize Ron Howard as a lovable little kid on *The Andy Griffith Show* and later as a lovable teen on *Happy Days*, two of the most popular shows in the history of television. But Howard wasn't content to be an actor; he became a successful director as well, helming more than 30 movies for TV and the big screen, including *Splash*, *Parenthood*, *Apollo 13*, and *A Beautiful Mind*.

Q. Who were Benjamin Kubelsky, Nathan Birnbaum, and Leslie Towne Hope?

A. You probably know these old-time radio stars as Jack Benny (Kubelsky), whose penny-pinching ways amused radio listeners in the 1930s and '40s; George Burns (Birnbaum), who teamed with his wife,  Gracie Allen, to tickle the funny bones of America; and Bob Hope (Leslie Towne Hope), who not only entertained radio audiences but was also a big star in movies and on television.

TRUE OR FALSE Lou Costello never made a movie without Bud Abbott.

ANSWER False. Considered one of the greatest comedy teams in the history of show business, Abbott and Costello made 36 movies together between 1940 and 1956. However, in 1959 Costello appeared solo in the comedy *The 30-Foot Bride of Candy Rock*. In the film, Costello plays a delivery boy who invents a machine that turns his girlfriend into a giant.

> ★★★ **FAST FACT** ★★★
>
> Mary Pickford, Douglas Fairbanks, and Norma Talmadge were the first three stars to leave their handprints outside Grauman's Chinese Theatre.

Q. Who was Erich Weiss?

A. Born Erich Weiss in 1874, the magician, escape artist, and performer Harry Houdini changed his name in 1894 when he launched his professional career. He took the name from French magician Robert Houdin.

Q. Which famous Method actor brought Tennessee Williams's Stanley Kowalski to life in stage and screen adaptations of *A Streetcar Named Desire*?

A. Marlon Brando. The most celebrated of American Method actors, Brando brought the Method to the forefront of American consciousness and culture with his raw, emotional portrayals. He won his first Oscar for his portrayal of Terry Malloy in Elia Kazan's *On the Waterfront*. Brando is considered by many to be the greatest movie actor of all time.

Dynamic Duos

* * * * * * * * * * * *

All of us have a favorite actor or actress, but did you know that sometimes directors have favorites, too? Check out this list of actor/director duos, from the silent era to modern day, and you might be surprised at just how many times they've worked together. (And some of them are still going!)

Director	Actor	Films Made Together
D. W. Griffith	Lillian Gish	30+
John Ford	John Wayne	21
Woody Allen	Mia Farrow	13
Michael Curtiz	Errol Flynn	11
Woody Allen	Diane Keaton	9
Spike Lee	John Turturro	9
Tim Burton	Johnny Depp	8
George Cukor	Katharine Hepburn	8
John Hughes	John Candy	8
Martin Scorcese	Robert De Niro	8
Wes Anderson	Owen Wilson	7
Billy Wilder	Jack Lemmon	7

Q. Who played characters Carnac the Magnificent, Aunt Blabby, El Mouldo, and the Maharishi?

A. Johnny Carson, the "King of Late Night." The Emmy-winning and Peabody Award–winning host of *The Tonight Show* for 30 years (1962–92), Carson played these personas and more on the show.

⭐ Oscar-nominated actor and seasoned helicopter pilot Harrison Ford is also a real-life hero. He has twice rescued stranded hikers in his Bell 407 helicopter: In July 2000 he air-lifted a hiker out of Table Mountain in Idaho, and a year later he rescued a 13-year-old Boy Scout who had gotten lost in Yellowstone Park.

Q. Which debonair Hollywood heartthrob participated in an experimental psychotherapy program in the 1950s that sent him on more than 100 hallucinogenic trips via LSD?

A. Cary Grant. Until 1966, the drug was legally available in the United States as an experimental psychiatric drug. Grant publicly discussed its therapeutic value, likening the hallucinations he experienced to the act of dreaming. While Grant spoke positively about LSD therapy, he also recognized the dangers of the drug and agreed with the decision to make it illegal.

"People forget that when you're 16, you're probably more serious than you'll ever be again. You think seriously about the big questions."

—John Hughes, director of *The Breakfast Club*, *Ferris Bueller's Day Off*, *Sixteen Candles*, and more (considered by many to be the creator of the modern teenage film)

Q. Who was the first African American to win an Academy Award?

A. Hattie McDaniels. McDaniels was named Best Supporting Actress in 1939 for her role as Mammy in *Gone With the Wind*. The first African American man to receive an Oscar was Sidney Poitier, who received the Best Actor statuette in 1963 for his role in *Lilies of the Field*.

> *"Hollywood's a place where they'll pay you a thousand dollars for a kiss and fifty cents for your soul."*
> —Marilyn Monroe

Q. In 1946, a suave, handsome crooner teamed up with a manic, insecure, aspiring funnyman. They went on to make 16 films together and became one of the most successful pairings in Hollywood history. Who was this duo?

A. Dean Martin and Jerry Lewis. Martin acted as the suave and unflappable straight man to Lewis's inept, immature, yet lovable bumbler.

★★★ **FAST FACT** ★★★

Charlie Chaplin was involved in numerous scandals during his lifetime—he was once accused of being a Communist and was also implicated in a paternity case. He made headlines even in death, when his coffin was dug up and held for ransom.

Q. Which Oscar-winning actor is related to Abraham Lincoln?

A. Tom Hanks. Hanks is Abe's fourth cousin, four generations removed. Lincoln's great-great-great-grandparents, William and Sarah Hanks, are also Hanks's ancestors.

TRUE OR FALSE Real-life husband-and-wife team Desi Arnaz and Lucille Ball starred on the classic radio program *My Favorite Husband*.

ANSWER False. Lucille Ball and Richard Denning starred as Liz and George Cooper on the original radio program. However, the program was the basis for *I Love Lucy*, one of the most-watched television sitcoms in American history, which premiered in October 1951 and starred Arnaz (Ricky) and Ball (Lucy).

Q. Who was comedian and ventriloquist Shari Lewis's fluffy alter ego?

A. The sweet sheep sock puppet Lamb Chop, which appeared on Lewis's musical-comedy television show throughout the 1960s. In 1992, Lewis created *Lamb Chop's Play-Along*, a children's show for PBS that won five Emmy Awards.

> ★★★ **FAST FACT** ★★★
>
> Actor Fess Parker played both Daniel Boone and Davy Crockett on television during the 1950s and '60s. Parker later became a real estate tycoon and vintner in California.

Q. Who was the host of *American Bandstand?*

A. Dick Clark. Clark, who has been called "America's oldest teenager," hosted the music-performance show on ABC from 1956 through 1989. Clark also hosts Dick Clark's *New Year's Rockin' Eve*, which has been on the air since 1972.

Q. Which humorous performer used to say that he "never met a man he didn't like"?

A. Will Rogers. The feeling was mutual: Rogers—one of the most popular celebrities of his time—was a cowboy, humorist, writer, performer, and actor. In 1934, he was voted the most popular male actor in Hollywood.

Q. Who was known for always ending her Saturday night TV show by pulling on her left earlobe?

A. Carol Burnett. *The Carol Burnett Show* ran for 11 seasons (1967–78). The ear tug was Carol's way of sending her grandmother a special message to let her know she loved her.

Q. Which two talk show hosts engaged in an epic battle over the seat of *The Tonight Show* in 2010?

A. Jay Leno and Conan O'Brien. When NBC announced that due to sagging ratings and complaints from affiliates, they'd be pushing *The Tonight Show*, then hosted by O'Brien, back into a post-midnight time slot to allow Leno's talk show to appear in late night, O'Brien walked away from the franchise. Leno was reinstated as *The Tonight Show*'s host, despite complaints and rallies from rabid fans of O'Brien. Conan soon returned to late night with his show *Conan* on TBS.

> *"Acting is the most minor of gifts. After all, Shirley Temple could do it when she was four."*
> —Katharine Hepburn

Q. Which '80s heartthrob is rumored to have hated the TV show he starred on so much that he lit his underwear on fire on set in an attempt to get fired?

A. Johnny Depp. When Depp joined the cast of *21 Jump Street*, he did so believing it would only be for one season, but when the show became a hit he was stuck. Eager to be taken more seriously, Depp got creative in trying to escape his contract, but it took four long seasons before he was finally free to leave.

★ In 1993, Grace Kelly became the first American actress ever depicted on a U.S. postage stamp. That same year, Monaco released a stamp bearing her likeness. In the United States, she was listed as Grace Kelly, while in Monaco, the stamp called her Princess Grace.

Q. Who was William Henry Brown?

A. Brown was the founder of the first African American theater troupe (1821). He named his New York theater the African Grove Theatre, and everything from Shakespeare to farce was performed there. The theater was so popular that it even attracted white audience members. Unfortunately, the company only lasted three years before the theater was burned down under suspicious circumstances.

Q. Who directed Disney's first feature-length cartoon?

A. Disney's landmark 1937 release, *Snow White and the Seven Dwarfs*, was directed by longtime animator and animation supervisor David Hand. The movie's visual beauty and mammoth commercial success inspired generations of future animators, including those who work today with computer-generated images instead of pen and ink.

TRUE OR FALSE Stanley Kubrick was such a perfectionist that one of the scenes from *The Shining* took more than 100 takes to shoot.

ANSWER True, but there's some debate over which scene was the real "winner." The book of Guinness World Records points to a scene featuring Shelley Duvall that is said to have taken 127 takes, but several people who worked on the film say the scene that took the longest to shoot was one featuring Scatman Crothers that required 148 takes. Either way, that's a lot of takes!

"The best time I ever had with Joan Crawford was when I pushed her down the stairs in What Ever Happened to Baby Jane?*"*
—Bette Davis, on her feelings about the rival actress

Q. Who entertained audiences as a singer, actor, and blackface comedian for nearly 50 years?

A. Al Jolson. The popular entertainer got his start in vaudeville and then moved on to musicals and, finally, movies. He is best remembered for his starring role in 1927's *The Jazz Singer*, the first feature "talkie," which revolutionized the movie business.

Q. Alex Trebek and Pat Sajak might be the first names that come to mind when *Jeopardy!* or *Wheel of Fortune* are mentioned, but who created those shows?

A. Merv Griffin. Griffin made a name for himself in the world of television through-out the 1960s, '70s, and '80s. He's not only the creative mind behind *Jeopardy!* and *Wheel of Fortune*, but was one of the most successful guest hosts of *The Tonight Show* during the Carson era and even had his own popular talk show, *The Merv Griffin Show*.

> ★★★ **FAST FACT** ★★★
>
> Actor Drew Barrymore not only comes from a long line of acting royalty, her godparents are Hollywood royalty too: director Steven Spielberg and actor Sophia Loren.

Q. Who was the first American actress to win an Olivier Award, England's equivalent of a Tony Award?

A. Patti Lupone. The two-time Tony Award–winner (*Evita*, 1980; *Gypsy*, 2008) was awarded the trophy for Outstanding Performance of the Year by an Actress in a Musical in 1985 for her performances in *Les Misérables* and *The Cradle Will Rock*.

EXPLORERS

* * * * * * * * * * * *

Since North America first became known, pioneers and explorers have blazed new trails and pushed the boundaries on land, at sea, and in the skies.

Q. Who said, "That's one small step for man, one giant leap for mankind"?

A. The first person to walk on the moon, Neil Armstrong. After these first famous words, Armstrong went on to describe what he saw. The second man on the moon, Buzz Aldrin, said, "Beautiful, beautiful. Magnificent desolation." Later that year, *Apollo 12* astronaut Pete Conrad, whose height was the shortest in the astronaut corps, jumped down from his lunar module and said, "Whoopie! That may have been a small one for Neil, but it's a long one for me."

Q. Who was the first person to drive an automobile across the United States?

A. Horatio Nelson Jackson. In 1903, Jackson drove from San Francisco to New York. This was no mean feat: Gas stations did not yet exist, and there were only 150 miles of paved roads in the entire country. Jackson proved it could be done, though he spent 63 days and a great deal of money doing it.

Q. Whom did President Thomas Jefferson hire to explore the newly bought Louisiana Territory?

A. William Clark and Meriwether Lewis. The duo set out in May 1804 to explore and map the American West.

Accompanied by a crew of explorers, they traveled from Missouri to the Oregon coast and back. Their 8,000-mile journey took two years, four months, and ten days.

TRUE OR FALSE A Kentucky slave was one of the lead explorers of Mammoth Cave in Kentucky.

ANSWER True. After Franklin Gorin purchased the cave in 1838, his slave, Stephen Bishop, explored far beyond the toured areas of the massive system of caverns, discovering many more miles of the cave no eye had yet seen. He created a remarkably accurate map and also served as a tour guide. Bishop is credited with opening the gateway for modern exploration of the cave.

> *"The wonders of the Grand Canyon cannot be adequately represented in symbols of speech, nor by speech itself. The resources of the graphic art are taxed beyond their powers in attempting to portray its features. Language and illustration combined must fail."*
>
> —John Wesley Powell, leader of the first known trip through the Grand Canyon

Q. Who gave "Old Faithful" its name?

A. In 1870, Henry Washburn, Nathaniel P. Langford, and Lt. Gustavus C. Doane set off on an expedition to explore what is now known as Yellowstone National Park. The men guided a group of more than a dozen explorers to discover a few of Yellowstone's most recognizable landmarks, including Old Faithful and Mt. Washburn, which the group named themselves.

Q. Who was the first woman to fly successfully across the English Channel?

A. Harriet Quimby. In 1910, Quimby became the first American woman, and the second woman in the world, to earn a pilot's license. She piloted a biplane across the English Channel on April 16, 1912. She died in July of that year when she fell 1,500 feet from her two-seater plane during an exhibition in Boston. She was 37.

> ★★★ **FAST FACT** ★★★
>
> In 1821, American seal hunter Captain John Davis was the first person to step foot on Antarctica.

Q. Which U.S. president was also a seasoned explorer and adventurer who was responsible for preserving much of America's natural landscape?

A. Theodore "Teddy" Roosevelt. Roosevelt had always been a man of action known for his adventures as a hunter, Rough Rider, and cowboy, so when he became president in 1901 it was only natural that he felt the need to preserve the landscape he loved so much. Under his presidency 150 national forests, 18 national monuments, and five national parks (including Grand Canyon National Park) were preserved, totaling more than 230 million acres of land.

★ Many people associate the discovery of the Cumberland Gap with Daniel Boone, but it was actually crossed by Dr. Thomas Walker of Virginia in 1750. Boone later widened the path, making it more accessible to travelers. Of course, Walker was not the first to cross the gap either—Native Americans had been using it for thousands of years.

Q. Who was the first person to reach the North Pole?

A. Robert E. Peary and Matthew Henson. Although most people recognize the name Robert Peary, he wasn't alone when he arrived at the North Pole in 1909. He was accompanied by Henson, an African American who was often dismissed as Peary's servant but who was finally recognized as codiscoverer and awarded a joint medal by Congress in 1944. Also with Peary and Henson at the pole were four Inuit guides.

⭐ In 1977, Sally Ride answered a newspaper ad placed by NASA, which was looking for new astronauts for the first time in a decade. Of the 8,000 who applied to the program, Ride was one of 35 accepted. Six years later, she became the first American woman in space when she launched on the space shuttle *Challenger* mission on June 18, 1983.

Q. Only one person has ever won the Medal of Honor, the Pulitzer Prize, and the Service Cross of the German Eagle. Who was it?

A. Charles Lindbergh. Aviator Lindbergh won the Medal of Honor for performing the first solo nonstop flight from New York to Paris (1927). The Germans were also impressed with him, and in 1938 Hermann Goering awarded the Service Cross of the German Eagle to Lindbergh, the only U.S. citizen to receive that honor. In 1954, Lindbergh's account of his famous flight, *The Spirit of St. Louis,* won him a Pulitzer Prize.

Q. How long did it take Nellie Bly to travel around the world?

A. Nellie Bly (*née* Elizabeth Cochrane) gained fame as an undercover reporter, writing an exposé on the asylum on New York's Blackwell's Island that brought about much-needed reforms in mental-health care. However, she is best known for her 1889 attempt to travel around the world in less than 80 days, surpassing the hero of Jules Verne's popular novel. And she did it: Traveling by steamship and railway, she beat the fictional Phileas Fogg with a round-the-world time of 72 days, 6 hours, 11 minutes, and 14 seconds.

The Mercury Seven

★ ★ ★ ★ ★ ★ ★ ★ ★ ★ ★ ★

These men were the first NASA astronauts:

1. Scott Carpenter
2. L. Gordon Cooper
3. John H. Glenn Jr.
4. Virgil I. "Gus" Grissom
5. Walter H. "Wally" Schirra Jr.
6. Alan B. Shepard Jr.
7. Donald K. "Deke" Slayton

Q. During their expedition across the American West in 1804–06, explorers Meriwether Lewis and William Clark were accompanied by a French fur trader and his young Shoshone wife. What was her name?

A. Sacagawea. Although she did not serve as a guide for the expedition, as is often reported, Sacagawea helped foster diplomacy with Native Americans, provided input on the best routes to take, and served as an interpreter.

Q. Each year the people of Ocean Shores, Washington, gather to celebrate "Undiscovery Day." They have a party and finish the evening by wading out into the ocean and shouting, "Hey, George!" Who are they shouting for?

A. George Vancouver. Vancouver surveyed the West Coast in 1791, sailing more than 30,000 miles and charting more than 4,000 miles of coastline, from California to Alaska.

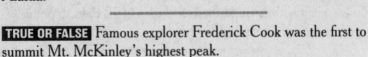

TRUE OR FALSE Famous explorer Frederick Cook was the first to summit Mt. McKinley's highest peak.

ANSWER False. Cook claimed to have conquered the mountain in 1909, but when he was caught lying about reaching the North Pole before Robert Peary, the truth came out about his mountaineering history as well. His climbing companion admitted that the peak they climbed was not only 19 miles away from the real point, but 15,000 feet lower as well. Hudson Stuck, who climbed the peak in 1913, is the real pioneer.

Q. What was significant about frontiersman Hugh Glass's 1823 trip from modern-day Lemmon, South Dakota, to Fort Kiowa?

A. Glass made the 200-mile journey after being mauled by a bear, robbed of his possessions, and left for dead. He crawled his way to the fort despite open wounds on his back and a broken leg. Today, a monument just south of Lemmon memorializes the brave adventurer.

Q. Who made a record-breaking sailing trip around the world in 1985?

A. Dodge D. Moran. Moran completed his solo journey in a mere 150 days, 1 hour, and 6 minutes. He broke 12 other records in the process, including being the first American to sail nonstop around the globe, fastest solo nonstop passage from Bermuda to Cape Horn, and fastest seven-day run during a single-handed nonstop circumnavigation.

Q. Who was known as "Lady Lindy"?

A. Amelia Earhart. America's most famous female aviator, Earhart was dubbed "Lady Lindy" (after aviator Charles Lindbergh) for her many accomplishments in the air. During the 1920s and '30s, Earhart set altitude and speed records and championed the place of women

> ★★★ **FAST FACT** ★★★
>
> In 2010, at the age of just 13, American Jordan Romero became the youngest person to summit Mt. Everest.

in the nascent field of aviation. Her brilliant career was cut short when she disappeared during an attempt to fly around the world in 1937.

Q. Neil Armstrong was the first person to walk on the moon. Who were the other crew members of *Apollo 11*?

A. Buzz Aldrin and Michael Collins. On July 20, 1969, Armstrong and Aldrin stepped out of the *Eagle* landing module onto the surface of the moon. Collins remained in the orbital command module *Columbia*. All of them received a congressional gold medal in honor of their historic work.

Q. Whose autobiography is titled *Alone*?

A. Admiral Richard A. Byrd. Byrd was a naval officer and pioneering American aviator and explorer who flew over the North and South Poles and traveled to Antarctica six times. His autobiography details, among other adventures, his solitary five-month stay in a meteorological station in Antarctica, during which he almost died of carbon monoxide poisoning.

> *"I have never been lost, but I will admit to being confused for several weeks."*
> —Daniel Boone

Q. Besides the indigenous people who had lived in America for centuries, who was the first American to reach California by land?

A. Jedediah Smith. Smith was the first American to cross the Sierra Nevada mountain range and the Great Basin, and was the first to travel up the California coast to the Oregon Country. Additionally, although it had been crossed before, Smith has been credited with effectively discovering the South Pass through the Continental Divide in 1824.

★ In 1846, George Donner assembled a group of 33 people to travel west from Independence, Missouri, to Sutter's Fort, California. Their attempted "shortcut" was actually 125 miles longer than the regular route. The Donner Party became stranded in the Sierra Nevada Mountains for four months. Two-thirds of the men and one-third of the women and children died on the journey. As reported by a group of rescuers, some of the remaining members of the Donner Party resorted to cannibalism in order to make it through the winter.

Q. Who is responsible for the settlement of Kentucky?

A. Daniel Boone. Boone recorded much about his exploration and settlement of Kentucky in his published personal account, *The Adventures of Daniel Boone*. His first expedition into the region took place in 1767, and he later colonized the area at the site of Boonesborough in April 1775. When he brought another party westward later that year, it included his family and solidified his role as a leader of the settlement of Kentucky.

TRUE OR FALSE Pikes Peak, a mountain in the Colorado Rockies, is named for the first man to successfully scale it.

ANSWER False. Although the mountain was originally named for the first man to climb it (James' Peak, after Dr. Edwin James, who reached the summit in 1820), the name was officially changed in the 1850s to reflect the name of the man who first *attempted* to scale it. Zebulon Pike spotted the towering mountain in 1806 and set out to climb it in November of that year, but a blizzard forced him back. The expedition Pike led when discovering the peak faced more difficulties than just the weather; they were also lost and then later captured by the Spanish.

Q. Who discovered the remains of the *Titanic*?

A. Robert Ballard. Expeditions from around the world searched for the wreckage in the North Atlantic, but it remained elusive until Ballard, an American undersea explorer, discovered it in 1985. In 1986, Ballard made the first detailed study of the ship, producing an in-depth photographic record of one of the most infamous disasters of the 20th century.

MUSICIANS

★ ★ ★ ★ ★ ★ ★ ★ ★ ★ ★ ★

From jazz to rock 'n' roll, country and western to opera, and beyond, American concert halls, stages, and radios have played the sweetest sounds imaginable. Tune in to find out if this chapter is playing your song.

Q. Which American performer is considered the most successful entertainer of all time by Guinness World Records?

A. Michael Jackson. On December 1, 1982, *Thriller* hit with the force of a tsunami. The album shot to number one on the Billboard charts and stayed there for 37 weeks. Never before or since has one album sold as well as *Thriller*—it went platinum 27 times, selling more than 50 million copies worldwide. Jackson quickly earned the undisputed title "King of Pop."

Q. Who was known as the "Man in Black"?

A. Johnny Cash. Cash, who has a place in both the Country Music Hall of Fame and the Rock and Roll Hall of Fame, joined the Grand Ole Opry in 1956 following the success of his hit single "I Walk the Line." But he only stuck around for two years. Though Cash would battle addiction, a bitter divorce, a controversial second marriage (to Nashville singer June

> ★★★ **FAST FACT** ★★★
>
> Elvis Presley was a twin: His brother, Jesse Garon, died at birth. Elvis was born 35 minutes later and given the middle name "Aron" in honor of his father's friend, Aaron Kennedy.

Carter), and several career missteps, his popularity surged in the 1960s and again in the 1990s before his death in 2003.

> *"Stick to driving a truck, because you're never going to make it as a singer."*
> —Memphis musician Eddie Bond to Elvis Presley in 1954

Q. Who called rock 'n' roll the "most brutal, ugly, degenerate, vicious form of expression it has been my displeasure to hear"?

A. Frank Sinatra. Nevertheless, ever the entertainer, he covered songs by Elvis, The Beatles, Paul Simon, and Joni Mitchell anyway.

Q. Which jazz clarinetist was known as the "King of Swing"?

A. Benny Goodman. The name was given to him by *Time* magazine in 1937. The Benny Goodman band made history in 1938 when they became the first jazz band ever to play at Carnegie Hall.

Q. Who was Max Yasgur?

A. Yasgur owned the dairy farm outside Bethel, New York, where An Aquarian Exposition: 3 Days of Peace & Music at the Woodstock Music & Art Fair—now known simply as Woodstock—was held in 1969. The city of Woodstock was supposed to host the festival, but when rumors spread that attendance could reach a million people, the city backed out. Yasgur saved the concert by hosting the more-than 500,000 attendees in his alfalfa field.

★ Louis Armstrong, one of the great American jazz musicians, often went by the nickname "Satchmo." When he was a child, his friends called him Satchelmouth because they thought his mouth was as large as a satchel. (He was also sometimes called "Gatemouth.") During an early tour of England, a music journalist mispronounced the moniker, shortening it to "Satchmo." Armstrong loved the new name and quickly adopted it.

TRUE OR FALSE Les Paul invented the electric guitar.

ANSWER False. The first person to successfully design and mass-produce the electric guitar was radio repairman Leo Fender. Together with musician/technician George Fullerton, Fender developed the Broadcaster in 1948. However, as early as 1941, musician Les Paul built a prototype of an amplified guitar: the Log. Paul continued to make refinements to the Log, and in 1952 the Les Paul Standard was put into production by the Gibson Guitar Company.

Q. Which big band musician participated in an unusual experiment at the Philadelphia Zoo in 1940?

A. Tommy Dorsey. The purpose of the experiment was to determine the effect of music on monkey behavior. According to a zoo employee, the first jazz number the orchestra played seemed to scare

★ ★ ★ **FAST FACT** ★ ★ ★

Prior to his appearance at Woodstock, Arlo Guthrie—the son of folksinger and composer Woody Guthrie—was best known for his 18-minute-long song (and subsequent film) "Alice's Restaurant," which describes how he avoided the Vietnam draft.

the monkeys, and they became quite agitated. But as soon as the band began playing its trademark "I'm Getting Sentimental Over You," the monkeys calmed down and became an interested audience.

⭐ Nat King Cole was the first African American man to attain mainstream acceptance as a pop singer. He made his breakthrough with the haunting "Mona Lisa." His much-heralded "Christmas Song" has become synonymous with the Yuletide season.

Iconic Jazz Musicians
★ ★ ★ ★ ★ ★ ★ ★ ★ ★ ★ ★

- Scott Joplin: ragtime composer around the turn of the 20th century

- Duke Ellington and Count Basie: leaders of swing bands of the 1920s and '30s

- Louis Armstrong: trumpeter and singer with the most recognizable voice in jazz

- Django Reinhardt: jazz guitarist of the '30s and '40s; inventor of the "hot jazz" guitar technique

- Cole Porter: composer and songwriter of the '40s whose hits include "I Get a Kick Out of You" and "It's De-Lovely"

- Charlie "Bird" Parker: lively bebop saxophonist and composer in the 1940s

- Miles Davis: trumpeter, composer, and bandleader in the '50s and '60s; influential in the creation of "cool jazz" and bebop

- Ella Fitzgerald: singer dubbed the "First Lady of Song" for her powerful and unique voice; one of the greatest scat singers of the 20th century

The Crooners

* * * * * * * * * * * *

A number of male vocalists were dubbed "the crooners" in the 1940s due to their smooth, soft, intimate vocal stylings. Among the most famous were:

- Nat King Cole (1919-65)
- Perry Como (1912-2001)
- Bing Crosby (1903-77)
- Dean Martin (1917-95)
- Frank Sinatra (1915-98)
- Mel Torme (1925-99)

Q. Scott Joplin was a self-taught pianist and composer who started out playing in dance halls and bordellos, but eventually he made his name by playing at the 1893 World's Columbian Exposition in Chicago. In what style did Joplin compose most of his music?

A. Ragtime. Joplin's bouncy and melodic music style was exemplified by his famous tunes "Maple Leaf Rag" and "The Entertainer."

Q. American symphonic composer Charles Ives was a realist who understood that many classical composers couldn't make a living composing. In what occupation did Ives earn his money?

A. As an insurance executive. Charles Ives composed many pieces, including four symphonies. But in 1906 he also founded the insurance company Ives & Myrick. One of his innovations in the insurance business was the development of estate planning.

"I stand for freedom of expression, doing what you believe in, and going after your dreams."

—Madonna, known as the "Queen of Pop"

Q. Who played on more number one singles than The Beatles, The Rolling Stones, The Beach Boys, and Elvis combined?

A. The Funk Brothers. In 1959, Motown founder Berry Gordy gathered the best of Detroit's jazz and blues musicians to begin cutting songs

★★★ **FAST FACT** ★★★

Stevie Wonder has won more Grammy awards than any other solo male artist (22); Alison Krauss has won more than any other woman (26) as a solo artist, collaborator with Union Station, and producer.

for his new record company. These session musicians included Richard "Pistol" Allen, Jack Ashford, Benny "Papa Zita" Benjamin, Jack Brokensha, Eddie "Bongo" Brown, Joe Hunter, James Jamerson, Joe Messina, Paul Riser, Earl Van Dyke, Robert White, and Eddie Willis. They performed on hundreds of Motown hits, including "My Girl," "I Heard It Through the Grapevine," and "Papa Was a Rollin' Stone."

Q. In 1935, a singing group named the Hoboken Four appeared on radio's Major Bowes' Amateur Hour and won the performance contest. While the Hoboken Four never reached stardom, one of its members did. Who was this famous singer?

A. Frank Sinatra. The vocal group auditioned for the show as Frank Sinatra and the 3 Flashes. Sinatra soon went solo, singing with the big bands of Harry James, Tommy Dorsey, and others. "Ol' Blue Eyes" also appeared in films, winning an Academy Award in 1953 for *From Here to Eternity*.

TRUE OR FALSE The Beach Boys recorded a song written by Charles Manson, the wild-eyed, murderous cult leader who ruled over a posse of deranged, drug-addled followers.

ANSWER True. Manson, who did have some natural musical ability, befriended Beach Boys drummer Dennis Wilson. Manson's song "Never Learn Not to Love," was on the B-side of the 1969 Beach Boys album *20/20*.

Q. Which celebrated opera singer, also known for his film acting and his radio show, was one of the founders of the American Guild of Musical Artists, the important labor union for solo performing artists?

A. Lawrence Tibbett, one of the finest baritones ever to perform at the Metropolitan Opera. His breakthrough role as Ford in Verdi's *Falstaff* in 1923 brought him widespread critical acclaim. He was nominated for an Oscar in 1930 for his role in *The Rogue Song*.

Patriotic Songs and Their Composers

★ ★ ★ ★ ★ ★ ★ ★ ★ ★ ★ ★

- "America, the Beautiful"—Katharine Lee Bates

- "God Bless America"—Irving Berlin

- "You're a Grand Old Flag"—George M. Cohan

- "This Land Is Your Land"—Woody Guthrie

- "Battle Hymn of the Republic"—Julia Ward Howe

- "The Star-Spangled Banner"—Francis Scott Key

- "America" ("My Country 'Tis of Thee")—Samuel Francis Smith

- "Stars and Stripes Forever"—John Philip Sousa

Q. Which set of brothers composed several musicals throughout the 1920s and '30s, including *Of Thee I Sing*, the first comedy ever to win the Pulitzer Prize?

A. Ira and George Gershwin. The brothers collaborated on a number of musicals, with George composing the music and Ira writing the lyrics. They worked with Fred Astaire and Ginger Rogers to make the musical film *Shall We Dance?* in 1937. One of George's most famous orchestral compositions is "Rhapsody in Blue."

George Gershwin

Q. Which rock 'n' roll musician is known for playing with The E Street Band?

A. Bruce Springsteen. Named after a street in New Jersey, The E Street Band garnered major media attention while backing Springsteen in the 1980s, most notably on the Boss's mega-popular album *Born in the U.S.A.*, which sold 15 million copies. But the band has played with many other musical giants since it formed in 1972, including Bob Dylan, David Bowie, and Aretha Franklin.

> **"We stuck to who we were at Motown, and the world came around."**
> —Berry Gordy Jr., founder of Motown

⭐ The first African American opera singer to perform at the New York Metropolitan Opera was Marian Anderson. Although Anderson sang for sold-out audiences, she often had to stay at the homes of fans because, at the time, Jim Crow laws prevented African Americans from staying in many hotels. The singer later served as a U.S. goodwill ambassador.

Musicians Who Have Died in Plane Crashes

* * * * * * * * * * * * *

- 1959 (Known as "The Day the Music Died"): Rock 'n' roll singers Buddy Holly (22), the Big Bopper (J. P. Richardson) (29), and Ritchie Valens (17)

- 1963: Country music singer Patsy Cline (30)

- 1967: Soul singer Otis Redding (26)

- 1973: Singer/songwriter Jim Croce (30)

- 1977: Rock 'n' roll band Lynyrd Skynyrd's lead singer Ronnie Van Zant (29), guitarist Steve Gaines (28), and vocalist Cassie Gaines (29)

- 1985: Rock 'n' roll singer Ricky Nelson (45)

- 1990: Blues guitarist Stevie Ray Vaughan (35)

- 1997: Folk singer John Denver (53)

- 2001: R&B singer Aaliyah (22)

Q. He may have been America's first hitmaker. This prolific songwriter wrote "Oh! Susanna" and "Old Folks at Home," among many others. Who was he?

A. Stephen Foster. Before sound recording, people bought sheet music like they buy CDs today. Foster's music was hugely popular. In the mid-1800s, a time when selling 5,000 copies made a song a hit, Foster sold 100,000. He saw some, but not much, profit from his work and died at age 37 with 38 cents in his pocket.

"If you talk bad about country music, it's like saying bad things about my momma. Them's fightin' words."
—Country singer Dolly Parton

Jim Henson, creator of the Muppets, recorded the popular songs "Rubber Duckie" (as Ernie) and "Rainbow Connection" (as Kermit the Frog). Both songs made it onto the Billboard charts: "Rubber Duckie" made it all the way up to number 16 in 1970, and "Rainbow Connection" peaked at number 25 in 1979.

TRUE OR FALSE Singer Aretha Franklin is known as the "Queen of Gospel."

ANSWER False. Franklin, a powerhouse performer and recipient of 18 Grammy Awards, is known as the "Queen of Soul." The title "Queen of Gospel" belongs to Mahalia Jackson, the world's first major gospel star and one of the only gospel singers to achieve mainstream success.

> ★★★ **FAST FACT** ★★★
>
> John Williams, winner of multiple Oscars, Grammys, Golden Globes, and Emmy awards, also composed the theme music for the Olympic Games and *NBC Sunday Night Football.*

Q. In the 1960s and '70s, which band was known for performing long, live jams of their combination of rock, folk, bluegrass, blues, country, jazz, psychedelia, and gospel?

A. The Grateful Dead, a band formed in 1965 by guitarist Jerry Garcia. The Grateful Dead toured regularly for its "Deadhead" followers until Garcia died in August 1995. The remaining members disbanded, but they later reunited to form the band The Other Ones, and they renamed themselves The Dead in 2003.

THE NATION'S FOUNDERS AND THE REVOLUTIONARY WAR

★ ★ ★ ★ ★ ★ ★ ★ ★ ★ ★ ★

The battle for freedom and independence left America with timeless warriors and brave leaders. How much do you know about this defining period in American history?

Q. Who was Crispus Attucks, and how did he contribute to the revolutionaries' cause?

A. Attucks, the son of a Native American mother and an African father (and possibly a runaway slave), led the colonial protest that resulted in the Boston Massacre. His bold 1770 protest against the continuing influx of British troops to the Boston area turned into a rock-throwing riot against armed soldiers. Some of the British soldiers retaliated with gunfire, killing Attucks and four other colonists.

Q. Who is known for the phrase "I have not yet begun to fight"?

A. John Paul Jones, America's first naval hero. Entangled in a fierce battle with the British frigate *Serapis* in 1779,

★★★★ **FAST FACT** ★★★★

Samuel Adams, an early and vocal dissenter of Great Britain's tyranny, has been called "The Father of the American Revolution."

Jones's ship, the *Bonhomme Richard*, had taken severe damage.

When the *Serapis*'s captain asked if he was ready to surrender, Jones yelled his immortal response: "I have not yet begun to fight!"

Words of Wisdom

★ ★ ★ ★ ★ ★ ★ ★ ★ ★ ★ ★ ★

Benjamin Franklin wrote, printed, and published *Poor Richard's Almanac* for 25 years, starting in 1732. He is well remembered for his pithy observations. Here are several of the best known:

• Never leave that till to-morrow which you can do to-day.

• Remember that time is money.

• There never was a good war or a bad peace.

• Early to bed and early to rise, makes a man healthy, wealthy, and wise.

• He that lieth down with dogs, shall rise up with fleas.

• God helps them that help themselves.

Q. Which Founding Father was called the "Master Builder of the Constitution"?

A. James Madison. At just 5'4", Madison may have been short of stature, but he is a giant in American history. He drafted the "Virginia Plan," which became the basis of the Constitution. He took the floor more than 150 times at the Continental Congress to push tirelessly for a strong central government. With Alexander Hamilton and John Jay, he also wrote The Federalist Papers, commenting on constitutional issues. In 1809, he became the nation's fourth president.

> *"Don't fire unless fired upon.*
> *But if they want a war let it begin here."*
>
> —Captain John Parker, commander of the militia at Lexington,
> Massachusetts, on spotting British troops (April 19, 1775)

Q. Whose name is synonymous with treason in the United States?

A. General Benedict Arnold. He was a friend of George Washington and a hero of the Revolutionary War, but when Arnold was passed over for promotion and received a court-martial charge for violating military regulations, he went over to the side of the British, committing treason against the colonies by leading raids on former allies and friends.

Q. Who said, "Give me liberty or give me death"?

A. Patrick Henry. The outspoken statesman was a self-taught lawyer and the first governor of the commonwealth of Virginia. But poor health forced Henry to turn down several key governmental positions, including secretary of state under George Washington, chief justice of the Supreme Court, U.S. senator, and U.S. minister to France. He was elected to the Virginia legislature in 1799 but died before taking office.

TRUE OR FALSE Betsy Ross designed the first American flag.

ANSWER False. Philadelphia seamstress Betsy Ross is known to have made flags during the revolution, but the claim that she created the first Stars and Stripes has been generally discredited. No one knows for sure who created the original design, but one likely possibility is writer, musician, and Declaration of Independence signer Francis Hopkinson, who was chairman of the Navy Board between 1776 and 1778.

Q. Who is often referred to as "the female Paul Revere"?

A. Sybil Ludington. Two years after Revere's 1775 ride, another American patriot made a similar ride to warn colonists of the approach of British soldiers. On April 26, 1777, the 16-year-old rode some 40 miles under cover of darkness (about twice the distance Revere had ridden), to alert the members of the militia to amass to defend their home of Danbury, Connecticut.

Q. Was Uncle Sam a real person?

A. Samuel Wilson (1766–1854), owner of a meatpacking plant that supplied rations to U.S. soldiers in the War of 1812, was the real-life inspiration for the character. The plant's barrels bore a large U.S. stamp on one side (for United States), and soldiers joked that U.S. really stood for their "Uncle Sam," who provided the food. The nickname stuck, but people who had never heard of Wilson thought it referred to the national government. The famous recruitment poster followed in 1917.

"'Tis done. We have become a nation."
—Benjamin Rush, on the ratification of the Constitution, July 9, 1788

Q. Who was the "Committee of Five" appointed by the Continental-Confederation Congress to draft a statement declaring the colonists' reasons for wanting independence?

A. John Adams of Massachusetts, Benjamin Franklin of Pennsylvania, Roger Sherman of Connecticut, Robert R. Livingston of New York, and Thomas Jefferson of Virginia. The committee subsequently asked Jefferson to write the Declaration of Independence.

*"When you are in a minority, talk;
when you are in a majority, vote."*

—Roger Sherman, the only member of the Continental Congress
who signed the Continental Association, the Declaration of
Independence, the Articles of Confederation, and the Constitution

Q. What was Molly Pitcher's true identity?

A. Many historians say the original Molly Pitcher was an Irish immigrant and Pennsylvania native named either Mary Hays or Margaret Corbin. The story credits Molly Pitcher with bringing water (the "pitcher" part explained) to the artillery gunners at the Battle of Monmouth (1778) during the Revolutionary War and replacing her wounded husband at his cannon. The name later became a generic term used to refer to women who carried water to men on the battlefield.

Benjamin Franklin's Epitaph

★ ★ ★ ★ ★ ★ ★ ★ ★ ★ ★ ★

"The Body of B. Franklin Printer; Like the Cover of an old Book, Its Contents torn out, And stript of its Lettering and Gilding, Lies here, Food for Worms. But the Work shall not be wholly lost: For it will, as he believ'd, appear once more, In a new & more perfect Edition, Corrected and Amended By the Author."

Q. Which patriot spy is said to have told his British executioners, "I only regret that I have but one life to lose for my country"?

A. Nathan Hale. No one knows for sure if the 21-year-old army captain actually spoke these words at the gallows, but it is believed he was familiar with the English writer Joseph Addison and was paraphrasing a line from Addison's play *Cato*, "What pity is it/That we can die but once to serve our country!"

TRUE OR FALSE The first submarine attack occurred during the Revolutionary War.

ANSWER True. Inventor David Bushnell created a watertight hull coated with tar, which he named "The Turtle." On September 6, 1776, the Turtle targeted the HMS *Eagle*, a flagship of the British fleet. Unfortunately, the Turtle exploded in New York Harbor before it could complete its mission of securing a cask of gunpowder.

★★★ **FAST FACT** ★★★

Virginia Dare was the first child born to English parents on American soil (1587). Her father was John White, commander of the settlement at Roanoke Island.

Q. Who killed Alexander Hamilton in a duel?

A. Vice President Aaron Burr. Revolutionary War veterans Burr and Hamilton had been enemies for years. In 1804, Burr challenged Hamilton to a duel. Shot in the abdomen by Burr, Hamilton suffered damage to this liver and spine and died 36 hours later. Burr was charged with murder but never tried, and he never held office again.

★ Thomas McKean's signature was not included on the official copy of the Declaration of Independence, even though he was a member of the committee and signed a copy. The lawyer from Delaware was one of the last people to sign the document, and because he signed after the official authentication date on January 17, 1777, his signature was not included on the official copy.

Q. Which Founding Father believed the Constitution should be rewritten every generation?

A. Thomas Jefferson. In 1816, Jefferson wrote a letter to historian Samuel Kercheval, stating his belief that each generation has "a right to choose for itself the form of government it believes most promotive of its own happiness...and it is for the peace and good of mankind, that a solemn opportunity of doing this every nineteen or twenty years, should be provided by the constitution."

"Our unalterable Resolution should be to be free. They have attempted to subdue us by Force, but God be praised! in vain. Their Arts may be more dangerous than their Arms. Let us then renounce all Treaty with them upon any score but that of total Seperation [sic], and under God trust our Cause to our Swords."
—Samuel Adams, letter to James Warren, April 16, 1776

Q. What did the Sons of Liberty accomplish in 1773?

A. A group of protesters known as the Sons of Liberty instigated the Boston Tea Party. Notable members of the Boston faction of the Sons of Liberty—though not necessarily those who directly participated in the protest—included John Adams, Samuel Adams, Benjamin Edes, John Hancock, William Mackay, James Otis, Paul Revere, Joseph Warren, and Thomas Young. The Sons of Liberty were the first to dump tea in the Boston Harbor in protest of high tea taxes and customs breaks that favored big British business.

TRUE OR FALSE George Washington was the only U.S. president who served in a military capacity in the Revolutionary War.

ANSWER False. Fifth president James Monroe was a soldier under Washington at the historic crossing of the Delaware River and the subsequent victorious attack on the Hessian encampment at Trenton, New Jersey. At the time, Monroe was just a teenager.

"Nevertheless, to the persecution and tyranny of his cruel ministry we will not tamely submit— appealing to Heaven for the justice of our cause, we determine to die or be free."
—American patriot Joseph Warren, 1775

Q. Did George Washington really tell his father, "I cannot tell a lie"?

A. The first U.S. president was renowned for his honor and virtue, but this line was nothing but a fabrication by a biographer who wanted to spice up Washington's image. Mason Locke Weems, a fiery pastor and bookseller, published *The Life and Memorable Actions of George Washington* in 1800, a year after Washington's death. It was an instant hit and was republished several times, with each edition boasting additions to a section titled "Curious Anecdotes Laudable to Himself and Exemplary to his Countrymen." The fabricated cherry tree story was included in the fifth edition (1806) and every edition thereafter.

⭐ The expression "rarer than a Button Gwinnett" actually refers to a real person: Georgia representative Button Gwinnett, a signer of the Declaration of Independence. Unfortunately, after he signed the document, he didn't have time to sign much else—he was killed in a duel less than a year later. Due to his untimely passing, the name Button Gwinnett became synonymous with scarcity.

TRUE OR FALSE Francis Scott Key wrote the music to "The Star-Spangled Banner."

ANSWER False. Although Key wrote the lyrics to the song (originally in the form of a poem), he did not compose the music. His lyrics were set to the tune of an old British song called "To Anacreon in Heaven."

Q. Who is the "Forgotten Founding Father"?

A. George Mason, a delegate from Virginia to the U.S. Constitutional Convention. In 1776, Mason wrote the Virginia Declaration of Rights, which inspired parts of the Declaration of Independence. Mason also helped draft the Constitution but ultimately opposed it because it lacked a Bill of Rights and made compromises to defend slavery. George Mason University in Fairfax, Virginia, is named in his honor.

Q. Who was the first publisher to print the Declaration of Independence with the signers' names?

A. Mary Katherine Goddard, a newspaper publisher and the first American postmistress. The British considered the Declaration a treasonable document, so for about six months it was circulated through the colonies without any signatures. Goddard printed the first copy of the Declaration with the identities of the writers revealed, forcing the Founding Fathers into the spotlight.

★ Henry Wadsworth Longfellow immortalized Paul Revere's midnight ride in a narrative poem. Although some dispute the veracity of all the poem's facts, "Paul Revere's Ride" (1863) preserved the story of the legendary figure's April 18, 1775, dash to warn his countrymen that the British were on the march.

POLITICS AND GOVERNMENT

★ ★ ★ ★ ★ ★ ★ ★ ★ ★ ★ ★ ★

Politics is a hot-button topic, no doubt. But America is a nation governed by the people, for the people, and—like it or not—the topic is here to stay. How much do you know about America's government and its political leaders over the years?

Q. Who was John Hanson, and why is he sometimes referred to as "the first real president"?

A. Hanson was a respected scholar and politician who was elected to Congress in 1779. He worked diligently to get the Articles of Confederation ratified, arguing that diplomatic recognition of the new country would follow. He was elected "President of the United States in Congress Assembled" in 1781, where he founded the national census and postal service, among other historic initiatives. While George Washington is officially the first president, having taken the oath of office in 1789, Hanson is a man who shouldn't be forgotten.

★ John Marshall went from growing up on the Virginia frontier to holding the office of chief justice of the Supreme Court of the United States. The fourth person to hold that job, he was appointed by President John Adams in 1801 and remained in the position for 34 years—longer than any other chief justice before or since.

Q. As a child, what did Sandra Day O'Connor want to be when she grew up?

A. Born in Texas in 1930 and raised on her family's ranch in Arizona, Sandra Day O'Connor grew up thinking she would go into the family business of cattle ranching. Instead, she discovered a love of law and eventually became the first woman ever to sit on the U.S. Supreme Court. She was nominated to the court by President Ronald Reagan in 1981 and served as associate justice until 2006.

Q. Who was the director of the FBI for almost 50 years?

A. J. Edgar Hoover. Hoover was appointed director in 1924 and held the position until his death in 1972. Among his accomplishments were the establishment of the world's largest fingerprint file, a scientific detection lab, and the FBI National Academy. He also used the organization's secret files to his benefit, blackmailing politicians to secure his powerful position.

> ★★★ **FAST FACT** ★★★
>
> Samuel J. Tilden, Grover Cleveland, and Al Gore all won the popular vote but failed to win enough electoral votes to be elected president (in 1876, 1888, and 2000, respectively).

"A wise and frugal Government, which shall restrain men from injuring one another, shall leave them otherwise free to regulate their own pursuits of industry and improvement, and shall not take from the mouth of labor the bread it has earned. This is the sum of good government."

—President Thomas Jefferson, in his first inaugural address

Politicians Who Were Rhodes Scholars

* * * * * * * * * * * *

- Cory A. Booker: Mayor of Newark, New Jersey (2006–)
- Bill Bradley: U.S. senator from New Jersey (1979–97)
- Bill Clinton: U.S. president (1993–2001)
- James William Fulbright: U.S. representative from Arkansas 1943–45; U.S. senator (1945–74)
- Dean Rusk: U.S. Secretary of State (1961–69)
- Strobe Talbott: Deputy Secretary of State (1994–2001)

Q. Who were the first women to serve in the U.S. House of Representatives and the U.S. Senate?

A. Jeanette Rankin (House) and Rebecca Felton (Senate). Rankin, a Republican from Montana, was elected to the House of Representatives in 1916. Felton was 87 years old when she was appointed to the Senate by the governor of Georgia. She served for one day: November 21, 1922.

⭐ One of the men named to the Warren Commission to investigate the assassination of John F. Kennedy had once been fired by Kennedy. Allen Dulles, a member of the 1963 commission, was the director of the CIA from 1953 through 1961, when Kennedy fired him following the bungled Cuban invasion known as the Bay of Pigs.

Q. Who were the only American citizens executed for espionage during the Cold War?

A. Julius and Ethel Rosenberg. The couple was executed in 1953 for passing information regarding atomic weapons to the Soviet Union.

Q. This first-term senator leapt to national prominence after a February 1950 speech in which he claimed that 205 Communists had infiltrated the State Department. For the next few years he was in the spotlight for his anticommunist crusade. Who was he?

A. Joseph McCarthy. McCarthy never proved a case, but his accusations were enough to ruin many a career. After public opinion turned against him in 1954, he was censured by the Senate for "unbecoming conduct."

TRUE OR FALSE The only people who appear on common U.S. currency are presidents.

ANSWER False. Alexander Hamilton appears on the $10 bill, and Benjamin Franklin is on the $100 bill.

Women Who Have Served as Supreme Court Justices
* * * * * * * * * * * * *

- Sandra Day O'Connor (1981–2006)
- Ruth Bader Ginsburg (1993–)
- Sonia Sotomayor (2009–)
- Elena Kagan (2010–)

Q. Who holds the record for the longest filibuster in Congress?

A. Senator Strom Thurmond. Thurmond conducted the longest filibuster ever on August 29, 1957. He spoke nonstop for 24 hours and 18 minutes in opposition to the Civil Rights Act of 1957. However, the bill passed two hours after he failed to convince any senators to change their vote on the bill.

Q. Who was Frank Wills?

A. Wills was the 24-year-old security guard who, on June 17, 1972, discovered that the locks on several doors in the Watergate hotel and office complex in Washington, D.C., had been taped. He removed the tape, but a few hours later, he noticed that they were taped again. Wills alerted authorities, who then surprised five men who were in the process of breaking into the offices of the Democratic National Committee.

Q. What prominent political family has been called "America's Royal Family"?

A. The Kennedys. Descendents of Irish-Americans Joseph P. Kennedy Sr. and Rose Elizabeth Fitzgerald include President John F. Kennedy, his brothers Robert and Edward (both U.S. senators), their niece Maria Shriver (award-winning journalist and former California first lady), and more. Stars of the Democratic party, family members held prominent positions in the federal government for 64 years—from 1947, when JFK was elected to Congress, through 2011, when Ted's son Patrick left the U.S. House of Representatives. Known for their wealth, good looks, education, and collective community service, the family has achieved iconic status. The Kennedys are also known for more than their fair share of tragedy, including the assassinations of John and Robert and four airplane crashes (three of them fatal).

> ★★★ **FAST FACT** ★★★
> President John F. Kennedy founded the Peace Corps in 1961.

Q. Who were The Keating Five?

A. The Keating Five were five U.S. senators accused of corruption in 1989. Alan Cranston, Dennis DeConcini, John Glenn, John McCain, and Donald W. Riegle were accused of interfering with the Federal Home Loan Bank Board's investigation of Charles H. Keating Jr., who had given them each $1.3 million in campaign contributions. After an investigation by the ethics committee, only McCain and Glenn were cleared of acting improperly.

"The Hollywood Ten"

★ ★ ★ ★ ★ ★ ★ ★ ★ ★ ★ ★

The Hollywood Ten was a group of McCarthy-era Hollywood writers and directors who were cited for contempt of Congress for their refusal to cooperate with an investigation that they considered a modern-day witch hunt. The artists were blacklisted and barred from working because of their suspected association with the Communist party at the height of the Red Scare.

1. Alvah Bessie
2. Herbert Biberman
3. Lester Cole
4. Edward Dmytryk
5. Ring Lardner Jr.
6. John Howard Lawson
7. Albert Maltz
8. Samuel Ornitz
9. Adrian Scott
10. Dalton Trumbo

Q. Which 1960s political activist titled his guide to governmental overthrow *Steal This Book*?

A. Abbie Hoffman, who was cheeky as usual when naming his book. The book was banned in Canada, and many stores in the United States refused to carry it for fear the title would prompt customers to shoplift. Had they carried the book, it might have been banned for other reasons—Hoffman describes how to make a pipe bomb, steal credit cards, and grow marijuana.

Q. Who said "Mr. Gorbachev, open this gate. Mr. Gorbachev, tear down this wall"?

A. President Ronald Reagan. On June 12, 1987, President Reagan challenged the General Secretary of the Communist Party of the Soviet Union to tear down the wall as a symbol of increasing freedom in the Eastern Bloc. The address is considered by many to have affirmed the beginning of the end of the Cold War and the fall of communism.

★★★ **FAST FACT** ★★★

Hollywood megastar and former Mr. Universe Arnold Schwarzenegger served as governor of California from 2003 to 2011. During his tenure, the Austrian-born star of the *Terminator* series was nicknamed "the Governator."

Q. Which military man was at the center of the Iran-Contra hearings in the 1980s?

A. Oliver North. The former Marine helped funnel U.S. profits from weapons sales in Iran to the Nicaraguan Contras. He also reportedly helped Panamanian dictator Manuel Noriega establish a covert network that supported the Contras. North was convicted of three felonies in 1989, but the convictions were later overturned.

"Hell, I never vote for anybody. I always vote against."
—Comedian W. C. Fields

★ The advent of television had a dramatic effect on the presidential race of 1960. Richard Nixon and John F. Kennedy were going head-to-head for the presidency and, for the first time in history, the debates would be televised. Those who listened to the first debate on the radio declared Nixon the winner, but audiences watching on TV saw a sickly, uncomfortable-looking Nixon debating against the handsome and healthy Kennedy and seemed swayed by what they saw. Kennedy went on to win the election, and from then on television played a central role in politics.

Celebrity Status

★ ★ ★ ★ ★ ★ ★ ★ ★ ★ ★ ★

Celebrities are no strangers to government, and more than a few have dipped their toes in the political pool to discover that perhaps they're more senator than starlet. Check out this list of celebrities who have been elected to office.

• Sonny Bono (singer/entertainer): mayor of Palm Springs, California (1988-92); U.S. congressman (1995-98)

• Clint Eastwood (actor/director): mayor of Carmel-by-the-Sea, California (1986-88)

• Al Franken (writer/actor/comedian): U.S. senator (2009-present)

• Ronald Reagan (actor): governor of California (1967-75); president of the United States (1981-89)

• Arnold Schwarzenegger (actor): governor of California (2003-11)

• Jesse Ventura (wrestler/actor): governor of Minnesota (1999-2003)

Q. Who was the longest-serving member in congressional history?

A. Robert Byrd. He earned the record on November 18, 2009, with 56 years and 320 days of combined service in the House and Senate. He also holds the record for longest unbroken tenure, another impressive feat. He began his service as a U.S. representative from West Virginia in 1953 and became a senator in 1959, where he served until his death in 2010.

Q. Who wrote the 1947 book whose title, *The Cold War,* added a new term to our national vocabulary?

A. Journalist Walter Lippmann. He coined the term to describe relations between the United States and the Soviet Union after World War II.

TRUE OR FALSE The youngest senator ever elected to office was 30 years old.

ANSWER False. Although the Constitution dictates that one must be at least 30 years old to run for the office, in 1818 John Henry Eaton became senator of Tennessee at the tender age of 28. It's unlikely that the Senate knew they were breaking the rules for young Eaton, thanks to the large families of the day and the poorly kept birth records. In fact, Eaton himself may not have known for certain if he was of age. It's presumed that his real birth date was discovered later.

> *"Government is not reason, it is not eloquence—it is a force! Like fire, it is a dangerous servant and a fearful master; never for a moment should it be left to irresponsible action."*
>
> —President George Washington

POP CULTURE

★ ★ ★ ★ ★ ★ ★ ★ ★ ★ ★ ★

From Facebook and fashion to comics and commercials, pop culture symbolizes America's lifestyles and leisure activities. The people and characters who influence the popular culture of America take us back through the decades.

"Show me someone who never gossips, and I will show you someone who is not interested in people."
—Barbara Walters

Q. Which television anchor's signature sign-off was "And that's the way it is"?

A. Walter Cronkite. More than just a television news anchor, Cronkite was the trusted face of American news from the 1950s through the early 1980s. Throughout his career with CBS News, Cronkite was a fearless reporter of the news, known for his level tone, authoritative voice, and unbiased reporting.

TRUE OR FALSE Superman was created by a teenager.

ANSWER True. In the 1930s, 19-year-old Jerry Siegel dreamed up the character. His friend Joe Shuster illustrated it. Interestingly, the original Superman was not a hero but a bald, telepathic villain with superpowers. The pair had no luck selling the idea for several years.

Q. Who was the most famous example of the term "pin-up girl" when it entered the English lexicon in 1943?

A. Betty Grable. The phrase first appeared in the armed forces newspaper *Yank* on April 30, 1943. During World War II, soldiers, who often lacked any real-life female company, "pinned up" pictures of Betty Grable and other Hollywood beauties inside their lockers.

In 1942, New York City Mayor Fiorello La Guardia called pinball "an evil menace to young persons because it develops the gambling urge in children." *The New York Times* reported, "One out of every three persons in the pinball business has been arrested at least once." Mayor La Guardia banned the game in New York City that year.

Hair Today, Gone Tomorrow
* * * * * * * * * * * *

Hairstyles come and go, but celebrity always remains in fashion. Match these celebrities to the hairstyles they either made famous or were famous for.

1. Billy Ray Cyrus
2. Jennifer Aniston
3. Dorothy Hamill
4. Jacqueline Kennedy
5. Mia Farrow
6. Farrah Fawcett
7. Amy Winehouse
8. Carol Brady (Florence Henderson)

A. The shag
B. The feathered flip
C. The pixie crop
D. The "Rachel"
E. The mullet
F. The bouffant
G. The beehive
H. The wedge

Answers: 1. E; 2. D; 3. H; 4. F; 5. C; 6. B; 7. G; 8. A

TRUE OR FALSE Mark Zuckerberg, the creator of Facebook, is the youngest billionaire in the world.

ANSWER False. While this used to be true, as of 2011 Dustin Moskovitz (founder of the software company Asana) nabbed the title—but only by a hair, as he's only eight days younger than

Zuckerberg (Zuckerberg was born on May 14, 1984; Moskovitz on May 22, 1984). Moskovitz has more ties to Zuckerberg than just his month of birth, however; the two were roommates in college, and Moskovitz was Facebook's third employee.

★ Walt Disney's TV portrayal of Davey Crockett, the "king of the wild frontier," kicked off a coonskin cap fad among children of the early 1950s. The TV character bore little resemblance to the actual historical figure, but no matter. Kids snapped up lunch boxes, puzzles, and coonskin caps and made Bill Hayes's recording of "The Ballad of Davy Crockett" number one on the music charts.

Q. Who was Abraham Zapruder?

A. On November 22, 1963, as President John F. Kennedy's motorcade passed through Dealey Plaza, bystander Zapruder filmed the event with a home-movie camera. The resulting movie, now famously called the "Zapruder film," was given to the federal government and launched several studies of and investigations into the assassination.

★★★ **FAST FACT** ★★★

Sexual Behavior in the Human Female, popularly known as the Kinsey Report, was published by biologist Alfred C. Kinsey in 1953.

Q. Which avant garde pop artist coined the phrase "fifteen minutes of fame"?

A. Andy Warhol, who said "In the future, everybody will be world famous for fifteen minutes." The phrase made its way into the popular vernacular, where it remains widely used.

Q. Which children's TV show host worked with puppets named Henrietta Pussycat and King Friday XIII?

A. Fred Rogers. Mister Rogers is best remembered for his cardigan sweaters and his line "Won't you be my neighbor?" He created more than 900 half-hour episodes of *Mister Rogers' Neighborhood* before his last show in 2001. The soft-spoken man from Pittsburgh was also a Presbyterian minister.

TRUE OR FALSE P. T. Barnum invented the modern circus.

ANSWER False. Phineas Taylor Barnum did not invent the modern circus. In fact, he did not even become a circus promoter until 1870, at age 60. Along with James A. Bailey, however, Barnum did give the circus much of its pizzazz and popularity. One of the most famous quotes attributed to Barnum is "There's a sucker born every minute." The only thing is, he never made that statement. It was actually uttered by a business rival, complaining that Barnum had maneuvered his audience away from him.

> *"How many actors have a shot at being part of something that became a part of pop culture? It's been very rewarding. I'm not getting the 20 million bucks for the new movies, but at least I'm getting warmth and recognition from people wherever I go."*
> —Adam West, the original "Batman"

Q. Is Betty Crocker a real person?

A. No. When thousands of letters were sent to General Mills in the 1920s, all asking for answers to baking questions, managers created a fictional character in an effort to give the responses a personal touch. The surname Crocker was chosen to honor a retired executive, and Betty was selected because it seemed "warm and friendly." At one point, a public opinion poll rating famous women placed Betty second to Eleanor Roosevelt.

Q. Which 1980s prime-time soap diva was Anne Bancroft's body double in the poster for the 1967 film *The Graduate*?

A. Linda Gray. Remember the famous promotional picture with Dustin Hoffman standing in the background, framed by Mrs. Robinson's stockinged leg? That shapely appendage really belonged to then-unknown model Linda Gray, who went on to become the long-suffering wife of J. R. Ewing on the TV show *Dallas*.

Q. Which American TV host first presented the Beatles on national television? (Hint: It's not who you might think.)

A. Jack Paar. Many people remember first seeing the Beatles on February 9, 1964, as guests on CBS's *The Ed Sullivan Show*. However, the group had already had its first American exposure on NBC's *The Jack Paar Program* some five weeks earlier, on January 3. While the Sullivan performance was live, the Paar show presented a film clip of a British concert from the previous November.

Q. Who did Robert Redford and Dustin Hoffman portray in *All the President's Men* (1976)?

A. Carl Bernstein and Bob Woodward, journalists who exposed the Watergate scandal in a series of articles for the *Washington Post*. Journalist and academic Ben Bagdikian considers

★★★ **FAST FACT** ★★★

Marilyn Monroe was the cover model on the first issue of *Playboy* magazine (December 1953).

Woodward and Bernstein's work "the single most spectacular act of serious journalism [of the 20th] century"—and public sentiment agrees.

Q. Who was known as "Public Enemy Number One" in 1930?

A. Al Capone. The notorious gangster ruled Chicago's underworld from the early 1920s through 1931, when he was convicted on multiple counts of tax evasion and sentenced to 11 years behind bars, ending up in Alcatraz.

TRUE OR FALSE Elliot Ness and his team, known as "the untouchables," who are generally credited with Al Capone's downfall, actually had very little to do with the conviction that took Capone off the streets.

ANSWER True. Ness did great work in impeding Capone's bootlegging racket with raids against illegal breweries and stills, but that's not what put Capone behind bars—it was tax evasion. While Ness worked on the bootlegging, the federal government worked on tax evasion, and in the end it was the government that won the day.

Q. Which prolific writer of horror stories and more has had more than 50 of his literary works filmed for the big screen or TV?

A. Stephen King. King sold numerous short stories to magazines before Doubleday published his full-length novel *Carrie* in 1973, launching a career that has spanned decades. Hollywood has clamored for the opportunity to turn his prose into box office gold.

TRUE OR FALSE Pat Sajak and Vanna White were the original hosts of *Wheel of Fortune*.

ANSWER False. Chuck Woolery and Susan Stafford hosted the show from its origin in 1975 until 1981 and 1982, respectively, when Sajak and White took the reins—or, rather, the wheel.

Q. Who successfully sued McDonald's for gross negligence after suffering third-degree burns from a spilled cup of coffee at the drive-through window?

A. Stella Liebeck, 79, of Albuquerque. Liebeck sued McDonald's in 1992 after she spilled a cup of the restaurant's coffee in her lap, burning herself so severely she required skin grafts and was hospitalized for a week. Two years later, a jury awarded her $160,000 in direct damages and $2.7 million in punitive damages, which a court later reduced to $480,000. Both parties appealed, and they eventually settled out of court for an undisclosed amount.

★ Fredericka "Marm" Mandelbaum was known as "the Godmother" in 19th-century New York. Mandelbaum ran a major criminal empire in the city and also operated a school for promising young shoplifters, pickpockets, and burglars.

TRUE OR FALSE Typhoid Mary was a real person.

ANSWER True. In the early 1900s, Mary Mallon cooked in the summer homes and kitchens of wealthy families. Wherever she worked, people came down with typhoid. By the time anyone made the connection, she had infected at least 26 people. Mallon refused to stop cooking, and she was arrested. Quarantined for years, she was released in 1910 when she agreed not to work as a cook again. However, under another name, Mallon took a job cooking in a hospital, causing a new typhoid outbreak.

Cute Couples

★ ★ ★ ★ ★ ★ ★ ★ ★ ★ ★ ★

These days it seems that a Hollywood couple isn't hot news unless the tabloids have coined a nickname for them. Although the couples come and go, the nicknames live on in tabloid and Internet blogging history. Here are a few of the catchiest:

• Bennifer (Ben Affleck and Jennifer Lopez)

• Brangelina (Brad Pitt and Angelina Jolie)

• TomKat (Tom Cruise and Katie Holmes)

• Taylor Squared (Taylor Lautner and Taylor Swift)

Q. Who wrote the poem "The New Colossus," which appears on the Statue of Liberty?

A. Emma Lazarus. The poem was originally written in 1883 as part of a fundraising event in the arts community to raise money for the completion of the statue's pedestal. Although the poem received little attention at the time, it was inscribed on a bronze plaque on the inner walls of the statue's pedestal in 1903. The Statue of Liberty had become a symbol of hope and freedom for immigrants, and Lazarus's poem seemed the perfect fit to forever memorialize that fact.

Actor James Dean died in a car crash shortly after getting a speeding ticket. While filming the movie *Giant*, Dean appeared in a PSA for auto safety that, ironically, ended with the line: "The life you save may be…mine."

Q. Which foul-mouthed New York call-in radio show host was the impetus for the term "shock jock"?

A. Howard Stern. The host of a nationally syndicated show on CBS radio's WXRK for 20 years, Stern, the self-proclaimed "King of All Media," now performs only for satellite radio station Sirius.

Q. Who was Clara Peller?

A. Peller played the feisty old lady in the Wendy's Hamburgers commercials of the 1980s whose three-word line, "Where's the beef?" became world-famous.

Q. Which figure skater was implicated in a conspiracy to harm a fellow competitor?

A. Tonya Harding. All of Harding's prior competitive achievements were overshadowed in 1994, when word of her involvement in an attack on fellow skater Nancy Kerrigan came to light. Harding's ex-husband and her bodyguard hired someone to break Kerrigan's leg so she wouldn't be able to skate. After the attack, Kerrigan went on to win an Olympic silver medal, while Harding was banned for life from participating in USFSA activities as a skater or a coach.

⭐ Oprah Winfrey's name is synonymous with success, but the name she was given at birth was not "Oprah," but "Orpah," after the biblical character. When the "r" and the "p" were accidentally swapped on her birth certificate, the new name stuck, and Oprah has run with it ever since.

Q. How did Jawed Karim's trip to the zoo in 2005 change the course of Internet history?

A. Karim's video of his outing became the first video posted to YouTube, on April 23, 2005. Karim, Chad Hurley, and Steve Chen founded the video-sharing website because they wanted to make it easy for the average computer user to upload and share video content. Now, 48 hours worth of video are uploaded to YouTube every minute.

Q. Which silent-film star was at the center of one of Hollywood's first major scandals?

A. Roscoe "Fatty" Arbuckle, a greatly successful on-screen comedian who even mentored Charlie Chaplin. In 1921, Arbuckle was accused of rape by a woman who then died of injuries believed to have been caused by him. The funny-man's days were over. He was eventually cleared of all charges, but it was too late; the damage had been done, and Arbuckle didn't set foot on the silver screen for ten years.

But Wait—There's More!
★ ★ ★ ★ ★ ★ ★ ★ ★ ★ ★ ★

Inventor Ron Popeil became a multimillionaire by pitching labor-saving, albeit unusual, devices on TV. Here are some of Ron Popeil's famous and infamous products:

• Veg-O-Matic

• Pocket Fisherman

• Smokeless Ashtray

• Inside-the-Shell Egg Scrambler

• GLH Formula Number 9 Hair System

• Showtime Rotisserie and BBQ Oven

• Electric Food Dehydrator

• Solid Flavor Injector

PRESIDENTS

★ ★ ★ ★ ★ ★ ★ ★ ★ ★ ★ ★

More than 40 men have held the office of president of the United States. History has recorded their public words and actions, but they all have personal stories as well. How much do you know about our nation's presidents?

Q. Most presidents have held other government positions before and after their time in office. Who is the only U.S. president to become chief justice of the U.S. Supreme Court?

A. William Howard Taft. The 27th president, who served from 1909 until 1913, was appointed chief justice in 1921 by Warren G. Harding and served on the court for nearly nine years.

★ The first U.S. president who was not born a British citizen was Martin Van Buren. Although every president has been born in North America, eight of the first nine presidents entered the world while the Union Jack still flew overhead. Van Buren was born after the Revolution, on December 5, 1782, in Kinderhook, New York.

Q. Andrew Johnson was Abraham Lincoln's vice president after the election of 1864, and after Lincoln's assassination, Johnson stepped into the presidency. Who became Johnson's vice president?

A. No one. There was no law in place to name a new vice president if the current one became president. The 25th Amendment, passed in 1967, states that in the event of a vacancy in the office of vice president, the president will nominate a vice president, whom Congress must confirm.

Q. Who is the only U.S. president to have written a Pulitzer prize–winning book?

A. John F. Kennedy. While recuperating in a hospital after spinal surgery, then-senator Kennedy wrote a collection of accounts describing decisive moments in the lives of famous politicians such as John Quincy Adams, Daniel Webster, and Sam Houston. The book, *Profiles in Courage,* was published in 1956 and won the Pulitzer the following year.

Q. George H. W. Bush and George W. Bush are America's second father and son to serve as president. Who was the first father-and-son pair?

A. John Adams and John Quincy Adams. The sixth president was the son of the second. Other presidents shared family ties, too: Teddy Roosevelt and Franklin Roosevelt were distant cousins (and Teddy was actually the uncle of Franklin's wife, Eleanor), and William Henry Harrison, the ninth president, was the grandfather of Benjamin Harrison, the 23rd.

★★★ **FAST FACT** ★★★

President Franklin Pierce gave his 1853 inauguration address completely from memory. It was over 3,000 words long.

Q. What does Harry Truman's middle initial, S, stand for?

A. Nothing. Truman's parents, Martha Ellen and John, were unable to decide on a middle name for their firstborn son. Instead, they settled on the letter S, which could represent either his paternal grandfather (Anderson Shipp Truman) or maternal grandfather (Soloman Young).

> *"Human rights is the soul of our foreign policy, because human rights is the very soul of our sense of nationhood."*
> —President Jimmy Carter

TRUE OR FALSE The Hoover vacuum cleaner is named after Herbert Hoover.

ANSWER False. Herbert Hoover was a successful engineer, but he had nothing to do with the machine, initially called a "suction sweeper." A few other things have been named after the 31st president, however: Hoover Dam, the "Hooverville" shanty-towns of the Great Depression, and the asteroid Hooveria.

Q. Which future president was born William Jefferson Blythe IV?

A. Bill Clinton. His father, William Jefferson Blythe III, died in a car accident before the future president was born. Clinton's mother, Virginia Kelley, later married Roger Clinton, and young Bill adopted his stepfather's surname.

> ★★★ **FAST FACT** ★★★
>
> President James Garfield could write Latin with one hand and Greek with the other—at the same time.

Q. Who was nicknamed "Silent Cal"?

A. Calvin Coolidge. "Silent Cal" Coolidge was known as one of the most laconic presidents. It is said that at a state dinner one night, a guest told Coolidge she had wagered friends that she could get at least three words out of him. Coolidge replied, "You lose."

Nine Presidents Who Never Attended College

★ ★ ★ ★ ★ ★ ★ ★ ★ ★ ★

- George Washington
- Andrew Jackson
- Martin Van Buren
- Zachary Taylor
- Millard Fillmore
- Abraham Lincoln
- Andrew Johnson*
- Grover Cleveland
- Harry S. Truman

*In fact, President Johnson never received any formal schooling; he credited his wife with teaching him to read and write.

TRUE OR FALSE President Woodrow Wilson appears on the $100,000 bill.

ANSWER True. Yes, there really are $100,000 bills. But these Gold Certificate bills, printed in 1934, have never been placed in general circulation—they are used for federal transactions. Other presidents who show up on high-denomination currency: William McKinley is on the $500 bill, Grover Cleveland is on the $1,000 bill, and James Madison shows up on the $5,000 bill.

Q. How many U.S. presidents have been born in Virginia, the state called "Mother of Presidents"?

A. Eight: George Washington, Thomas Jefferson, James Madison, James Monroe, William Henry Harrison, John Tyler, Zachary Taylor, and Woodrow Wilson. (Of course, at the time some were born in Virginia, it was still a colony of England and not yet a state.)

⭐ President Millard Fillmore established the White House library. Before his term in office, there was no permanent collection of books in the White House.

Q. Which U.S. president served the shortest term?

A. William Henry Harrison. Though some believed he died of a cold he caught during his inauguration on March 4, 1841, his death was due to pneumonia, which is caused by a virus, not cold weather. He died on April 4, after just 31 days in office.

⭐⭐⭐ **FAST FACT** ⭐⭐⭐

Andrew Jackson was the first common man to become president (1829). All those before him came from wealthy families, but Jackson was born poor and had to make his own way in the world.

"If an individual wants to be a leader and isn't controversial, that means he never stood for anything."
—President Richard Nixon

Q. Although the public remained unaware at the time, Woodrow Wilson suffered a debilitating stroke while in office. Who is said to have made most of the president's decisions during this time?

A. First lady Edith Wilson. When the president suffered a paralytic attack in 1919, Mrs. Wilson sequestered her husband during his illness and, while she claimed his brain was "clear and untouched," replaced sitting cabinet members with Wilson loyalists and often signed his name to veto messages and legislation.

TRUE OR FALSE John F. Kennedy was the youngest person to serve as the president of the United States.

ANSWER False. At age 43, John F. Kennedy was the youngest person to be *elected* president, but Theodore Roosevelt took the oath of office on September 14, 1901, when he was just 42 years and 10 months old. He had been vice president and became president after William McKinley was assassinated.

Q. Who created the interstate highway system?

A. President Dwight D. Eisenhower. Motivated by a most unpleasant cross-country trip with an army convoy in 1919, and inspired by the massive autobahns he had seen in Germany, in 1956 Eisenhower achieved passage of the Federal-Aid Highway Act, the first decisive step in the construction of America's 46,000-mile network of interstate highways.

Q. Who pardoned Richard Nixon for his role in the Watergate scandal?

A. President Gerald Ford. Ford, who succeeded Nixon in the presidency, claimed that it was in the best interests of the country to move on from the ordeal rather than wallow in what could have been years of legal wrangling over Nixon's guilt or innocence.

Q. Who made Christmas an official U.S. holiday?

A. President Ulysses S. Grant, who signed it into law in 1870. It wasn't until 1890 that every state followed suit and declared it a holiday.

Q. Four U.S. presidents have been assassinated while in office: Abraham Lincoln, James Garfield, William McKinley, and John F. Kennedy. Which one lived the longest before succumbing to his injuries?

> ★★★ **FAST FACT** ★★★
>
> Chester A. Arthur was not pleased with the shabby condition of the White House when he moved in in 1881. He hired famed New York designer Louis Tiffany to redecorate it.

A. James Garfield. Lincoln was shot in the evening and passed away the following morning. McKinley died of gangrene infection eight days after being shot. Kennedy was pronounced dead half an hour after being struck by gunshots. But Garfield lingered for more than 11 weeks before dying of his gunshot wounds.

★ Thomas Jefferson is considered by many to be America's original Renaissance man—inventor, architect, writer, statesman, gourmet, naturalist, and one of the great political theorists in American history. However, he remains one of the great contradictions as well. Though he wrote the Declaration of Independence and was at one time the most prominent opponent of slavery—calling it an "abominable crime"—he was also a slaveholder, owning up to 300 slaves at one time, and is rumored to have fathered several children with one of his slaves.

Q. Whose idea was "The Great Society"?

A. President Lyndon Johnson. "The Great Society," Johnson said, "rests on abundance and liberty for all." Federal spending on health, education, welfare, and Social Security more than doubled during his administration, and the 1964 Civil Rights

Act, the Voting Rights Act of 1965, the 1968 Civil Rights Act, and the Endangered Species Act were passed.

⭐ As a child, William Howard Taft loved to play baseball. He was a great hitter but not a great runner because of his size. The tradition of the president throwing out the first ball on baseball's opening day began with Taft.

Q. Which U.S. president's corpse was moved, displaced, and nearly stolen 17 times before it was finally laid to rest?

A. Abraham Lincoln. Fortunately, the 1876 plan formulated by two criminals to break into Lincoln's tomb, kidnap the body, and hold it for ransom was foiled. In 1901, Abraham Lincoln found his final resting place in a cement vault in Oak Ridge Cemetery near Springfield, Illinois.

Q. Which two former presidents died on the same day?

A. John Adams and Thomas Jefferson. Both died on July 4, 1826, fifty years to the day after the official signing of the Declaration of Independence.

★★★ **FAST FACT** ★★★

The only president never to have won a national election was Gerald Ford, who took office after President Richard Nixon resigned in 1974, and served only one term.

Q. Who is the only president to serve two nonconsecutive terms?

A. Grover Cleveland. Cleveland was both the 22nd and the 24th president of the United States. He served from 1885 to 1889 and from 1893 to 1897.

★ After serving as president from 1825 to 1829, John Quincy Adams was elected to the House of Representatives in 1830. He served as a representative for 17 years, until his death in 1848. Another former president, Andrew Johnson, later served in the U.S. Senate after his presidency.

Q. Which president, known as "The Great Communicator," was the only president who was once a movie actor?

A. Ronald Reagan. Reagan appeared in more than 50 films. In one movie, *Bedtime for Bonzo*, Reagan even acted with a chimpanzee. During World War II, Reagan made training films for the war effort.

Q. Which president was known for his "fireside chats"?

A. Franklin D. Roosevelt. Roosevelt often gave speeches on the radio, which came to be called "fireside chats." In these informal talks, it seemed as if the president were speaking directly to each American. Roosevelt explained to people what he was trying to do and often outlined what they could do to help. The president's smooth voice reassured worried Americans during the Great Depression and, later, World War II.

> ★★★ **FAST FACT** ★★★
>
> James Buchanan was the only president who never married. His niece, Harriet Lane Johnston, served as his first lady.

Q. Who was nicknamed "Old Rough and Ready"?

A. Zachary Taylor. While many military leaders were concerned about handsome uniforms and polished boots, General Taylor often wore untidy farm clothes into battle. He was called "Old Rough and Ready" because of his appearance and his willingness to fight side-by-side with his troops.

TRUE OR FALSE The teddy bear was named after President Theodore "Teddy" Roosevelt.

ANSWER True. In 1902, Teddy went on a bear hunt in Mississippi. The only bear he found was just a cub, and he refused to shoot it. A newspaper ran a cartoon about it, and a toymaker in Brooklyn, New York, put the cartoon next to a stuffed bear, calling it "Teddy's Bear." The teddy bear was born.

Presidents Who Were Generals in the U.S. Army

★ ★ ★ ★ ★ ★ ★ ★ ★ ★ ★ ★

- George Washington
- Andrew Jackson
- William Henry Harrison
- Zachary Taylor
- Franklin Pierce
- Andrew Johnson
- Ulysses S. Grant
- Rutherford B. Hayes
- James A. Garfield
- Chester A. Arthur
- Benjamin Harrison
- Dwight D. Eisenhower

"And I will do everything that I can as long as I am President of the United States to remind the American people that we are one nation under God, and we may call that God different names but we remain one nation."
—President Barack Obama

SCIENTISTS AND INVENTORS

★ ★ ★ ★ ★ ★ ★ ★ ★ ★ ★ ★

America is a nation of innovators and inventors. Pioneering advancements in transportation, communications, medicine, chemistry, digital technology, and many other fields, Americans have often been at the forefront of progress.

"I think there is a world market for maybe five computers."
—Thomas Watson, chairman of IBM, 1943

Q. Who discovered the existence of galaxies beyond the solar system?

A. Astronomer Edwin Hubble, who studied science and mathematics at the University of Chicago and attended Oxford University on a Rhodes scholarship. Hubble then returned to the States to continue his work in astronomy. His name lives on, of course, with the Hubble Space Telescope, which has been orbiting our planet since 1990.

★ Intending to create a wallpaper cleaner, Joseph and Noah McVicker invented Play-Doh in 1955. Initially available in only one color (off-white) and in a 1.5-pound can, Play-Doh now comes in a rainbow of colors. The recipe remains a secret, but more than 700 million pounds of this nontoxic goop have been sold since its introduction.

Q. In 1848, Charles Burton invented something that caused a stir in his home of New York City. Initially, New Yorkers protested against his invention because pedestrians tended to get hit with it. What did he invent?

A. A baby carriage. Charles Burton left New York for England, where he opened a factory to make "perambulators." His customers included such royalty as England's Queen Victoria and Queen Isabella II of Spain.

Q. Which early-20th-century inventor is known primarily for his work with peanuts and sweet potatoes?

A. George Washington Carver. Carver's agricultural innovations helped rescue the South from its dependence on cotton—he introduced hundreds of uses for peanuts and sweet potatoes. Furthermore, he encouraged Southern farmers to cultivate these crops, thereby diversifying their farms, replenishing the soil, and protecting their cash crops from natural disasters.

★★★ **FAST FACT** ★★★

Robert Fulton's modifications of the *North River Steamboat* (later known as the *Clermont*) made boats with steam engines efficient and viable as commercial vessels and ushered in a new era of water travel in the early 1800s.

Q. Who created the Franklin stove, America's first public library, and the lightning rod?

A. In addition to his many other accomplishments, Benjamin Franklin was very adept at developing new devices and institutions. From an early age, he immersed himself in the technical and journalistic facets of printing. He soon became a master printer, as well as a writer, first publishing *Poor Richard's Almanac* in 1732. Living in Philadelphia, he improved the efficiency of heating with the Franklin stove, originated America's first public library, and founded the city's first fire department. His fascination with electricity led to the development of the lightning rod and his famous experiments with lightning and kites in 1752.

> *"We scientists are the only people who are not bored, the only adventurers of modern times, the real explorers—the fortunate ones."*
>
> —1960 Nobel Laureate Willard F. Libby

Q. Who discovered DNA?

A. Francis Crick and James Watson. The pair discovered the structure of DNA in the 1950s, describing it as a double helix, a twisting ladder of nucleotide chains. English scientists Maurice Wilkins and Rosalind Franklin contributed research that was instrumental in Crick and Watson's discovery.

⭐ Brothers Wilbur and Orville Wright spent years concocting theories, conducting informal tests, and experimenting with hundreds of glider flights, refining their ideas about flight. On December 17, 1903, Orville Wright climbed into a motor-powered glider and made the world's first machine-powered flight. It lasted only 12 seconds, but it was successful enough to convince the brothers they were on the right track.

Q. The RCA corporation spent millions to develop television technology, but who developed the basic working theory?

A. Philo T. Farnsworth. Farnsworth was just 14 years old when he realized that an image could be scanned by a beam of electrons controlled by an electromagnetic field. In 1927, shortly after he turned 21, he succeeded in creating a groundbreaking electronic transmission that was the beginning of television as we know it.

TRUE OR FALSE Henry Ford invented the automobile.

ANSWER False. Contrary to popular belief, Ford did not invent the automobile, nor did he invent the assembly line (though he improved the concept). He introduced the Model T in 1908, and its assembly-line production by unskilled laborers allowed productivity to skyrocket and prices to plummet. His vision literally changed the landscape of the nation, bringing his workers into the middle class and making the automobile affordable to more than just the upper class.

1960 Men of the Year
★ ★ ★ ★ ★ ★ ★ ★ ★ ★ ★ ★

In 1960, *Time* magazine named U.S. scientists their "Men of the Year," saying, "Their work shapes the life of every human presently inhabiting the planet" and "the heart of scientific inquiry now beats strongest in this country." They were represented by 15 scientists, including:

- John Enders—medical scientist, created vaccine for measles

- Joshua Lederberg—molecular biologist, pioneer in developing artificial intelligence

- Willard Libby—physical chemist, developed radiocarbon dating

- Emilio Segrè—physicist, led Manhattan Project and discovered the anti-proton

- William Shockley—physicist/inventor, coinvented the transistor

- James Van Allen—space scientist, discovered Earth's radiation belts

Q. Who developed a silicone-based elastic polymer that became a popular toy?

A. James Wright. Silly Putty was developed in 1943 when Wright, a General Electric researcher, was seeking a synthetic rubber substitute. His silicone-based polymer was elastic, could bounce, was easily molded, and always held its shape. Parents liked the fact that the putty was nontoxic and nonirritating. Since its debut as a toy in 1950, more than 300 million eggs of Silly Putty have been sold.

> ★ ★ ★ **FAST FACT** ★ ★ ★
>
> In December 1982, Barney Clark, a Seattle dentist, was the first recipient of an artificial heart. Dr. Robert Jarvik, a graduate of the University of Utah, designed the heart.

Q. Who was known as the "Wizard of Menlo Park"?

A. Thomas Alva Edison, the most prodigious inventor in American history. He patented 1,093 inventions from 1881 through 1933, including the incandescent lightbulb and the phonograph. Edison's laboratories were also instrumental in devising the motion picture camera and viewer. In fact, the first motion picture to be copyrighted was created in the Edison labs.

★ Bill Gates is the "computer geek" who revolutionized the way people use computers and how businesses conduct business. In other words, he changed the world forever, founding Microsoft, designing MS-DOS and Windows, and founding the philanthropic Gates Foundation.

Q. Who sent a telegraph that asked, "What hath God wrought?"

A. Samuel F. B. Morse. Morse invented the telegraph in 1844, sending a series of electrical dots and dashes along a copper wire strung between Washington, D.C., and Baltimore.

Q. Who invented the air conditioner?

A. Willis H. Carrier. When Carrier built the first effective air-conditioning unit in 1902, his goal was not to cool the room to make it comfortable for human beings; rather, he was trying to prevent paper from contracting and expanding in hot and humid conditions. The first commercial use of air-conditioning to make people more comfortable came 15 years later.

Q. Every year the city of Farmington, Maine, celebrates "Chester Greenwood Day." Who was Chester Greenwood?

A. He invented earmuffs. When he turned 15 in 1873, Greenwood received ice skates. To keep his ears from freezing while he skated, he rigged up some beaver fur and wire, which he called "ear mufflers." He patented his invention in 1877.

Inventors Who Dropped Out of School

★ ★ ★ ★ ★ ★ ★ ★ ★ ★ ★ ★

- George Eastman (founder of Kodak) was a high school dropout.
- Thomas Edison dropped out after only three months of formal education and was home-schooled by his mother.
- Benjamin Franklin spent two years at the Boston Latin School before dropping out at age 10.
- Isaac Singer dropped out of elementary school.

Tragic Irony
* * * * * * * * * * * *

Inventors do a lot to progress humanity, but sometimes in doing so they pay the ultimate price. These American inventors were killed by their own inventions:

• Thomas Midgley Jr.—After contracting polio, he devised a pulley system that helped others lift him from the bed. Tragically, he became tangled in it and was strangled to death.

• Horace Lawson Hunley—Inventor of the first submarine, he died when the sub sank during a routine test.

• Henry Smolinski—In trying to invent a flying car based on the Ford Pinto, Smolinski was killed during a test flight when the vehicle crashed.

Q. Who invented windshield wipers?

A. Mary Anderson. While taking a trip from Alabama to New York City just after the turn of the 20th century, she noticed that when it rained, drivers had to open their car windows to see. Anderson invented a swinging-arm device with a rubber blade that the driver operated by using a lever. In 1903, she received a patent for what became known as the windshield wiper; by 1916, it was standard on most vehicles.

TRUE OR FALSE Jonas Salk patented the first vaccine for polio.

ANSWER False. Salk developed the killed-virus polio vaccine in 1954 but refused to patent it because he wanted it to be distributed as quickly as possible. Albert B. Sabin pioneered the oral live-virus polio vaccine in the late 1950s.

Q. Did Isaac Singer invent the sewing machine?

A. No, but he perfected the first commercially successful one. Europeans had been attempting to build a sewing machine for hundreds of years without success. In 1834, American Walter Hunt built the first functional sewing machine, but he never patented it. In 1846, Elias Howe was issued the first American patent for a sewing machine, and then in 1851 Singer received a patent for his version.

Q. Percy Spencer's most famous invention, which weighed 750 pounds and cost $5,000 when it was first produced in 1947, didn't have much of a market. What was it?

A. The microwave oven. Spencer had been experimenting with a new vacuum tube called a magnetron and became intrigued when the candy bar in his pocket began to melt. He tried another experiment with popcorn, and when it popped, he knew he was onto something. Thankfully, a countertop version was introduced in 1967, which led to the microwave ovens of today.

Q. How did Samuel Colt's 1830 missionary trip to Africa lead to the revolutionizing of the Wild West?

A. As he watched the wheel of the ship turn, Colt noticed that the spokes aligned with a clutch that locked them into place at any time. Inspired, he applied the same principle to firearms, creating the first revolver. It was the only gun at the time that could fire more than one shot without having to be reloaded.

"Never doubt that a small group of thoughtful, committed citizens can change the world. Indeed, it is the only thing that ever has."
—Margaret Mead, 20th-century anthropologist

Q. A written language is often considered a building block of civilization. Who was the only person to single-handedly invent a written language and bring literacy to a culture?

A. Sequoyah. The son of a Cherokee woman and a Virginia trader, Sequoyah was fascinated by settlers' books. He divided the sounds of spoken Cherokee into 86 syllables and designed a symbol for each. In 1821 he introduced the script to his leaders, who mastered it in a week and gave him permission to teach their people.

TRUE OR FALSE Alexander Graham Bell, inventor of the telephone, was born deaf.

ANSWER False. Bell's hearing was fine, but with a wife and mother who were unable to hear, he was much interested in the deaf. He invented a phonoautograph—a device that reads vibrations from voices—to help deaf students. This invention evolved into the telephone.

Q. Which American microbiologist developed disease-resistant wheat varieties that saved billions of people from starvation?

A. Norman Ernest Borlaug. The microbiologist and agricultural scientist was instrumental in developing high-yield, disease-resistant wheat varieties in Latin America, Africa, and Asia. Borlaug effectively saved billions of people from starvation and was awarded the Nobel Peace Prize in 1970. According to the Congressional Tribute to Dr. Norman E. Borlaug Act of 2006, "Dr. Borlaug has saved more lives than any other person who has ever lived."

THE WILD WEST

★ ★ ★ ★ ★ ★ ★ ★ ★ ★ ★ ★

Perhaps no other time in America's history is as steeped in myth, legend, and adventure as the pioneering age of the Wild West. Mount up the horses and move out the wagon train—it's time to test your frontier knowledge.

Q. One of the most famous women of the Wild West was legendary for her target-shooting ability. In fact, she could hit a thrown playing card with a dozen bullets before it landed on the ground. Who was this renowned sharpshooter?

A. Annie Oakley. Born in a rustic log cabin, Phoebe Anne Oakley Mosee learned to use a rifle at the age of six to help feed her family. She soon became a professional game hunter and joined Buffalo Bill's Wild West show at the age of 25.

TRUE OR FALSE Horace Greeley, influential founder and editor of the *New York Tribune*, was the source of the statement "Go West, young man."

ANSWER False. Although this statement, heard frequently in the 19th century, has often been credited to Greeley, it was first penned by Indiana reporter John Soule in 1851. Greeley popularized the quote, but he did try to provide Soule with proper credit.

★ Geronimo's real name was *Goyahkla*, Native American for "one who yawns." A leader of the Chiricahua Apache people, Geronimo was never a chief in the formal sense, but his people regarded him as a seer, medicine man, spiritual guide, and leader in battle.

Q. Who killed the outlaw Jesse James?

A. Bob Ford, fellow member of the James–Younger gang. Ford was Jesse James's friend and partner in crime. He even lived with James, but at the same time he was plotting to kill the outlaw to claim the $10,000 reward. As James stood on a chair to dust a picture in his own home in St. Joseph, Missouri, Ford saw his chance and took it, shooting James in the back of the head on April 3, 1882.

Q. Who was the first artist to record Western tribal groups and their way of life?

A. George Catlin. In 1824, Catlin encountered a group of 15 Western chieftains who were on a tour of the East, and he resolved to preserve on canvas the Native Americans of the West before they became "corrupted by civilization." In six years Catlin produced more than 600 scenes and portraits of 48 tribal groups.

Q. Who is the "dead man's hand" named after?

A. Wild Bill Hickok. The infamous frontiersman was shot in the back of the head and killed while playing poker in Deadwood in 1876. At the time he was shot, he was holding two aces and two eights—the cards that are known to this day as the "dead man's hand."

Q. Not everyone who contributed to taming the Wild West did so behind the barrel of a gun. Joseph Glidden, a very "un-cowpoke" sort of man, created something to make life easier on the frontier. What was it?

A. Barbed wire. Glidden, an Illinois farmer, patented barbed wire in 1874, realizing that wood was too expensive for cattle ranchers to use for fencing. In just a few years, Glidden's plant was producing more than 80 million pounds of barbed wire annually.

"We are rough men and used to rough ways."
—Bob Younger, member of the James-Younger gang

Q. Many tales of the Wild West feature the thrilling stories of lawman Bat Masterson. The famous sheriff eventually tired of gunfights, however, and changed careers. What did he become?

A. After serving as sheriff of Ford County, Kansas, and helping bring law and order to Tombstone, Arizona, Masterson moved to New York City, where he became a sports-writer for the *New York Morning Telegraph* and gained a reputation as an expert on boxing.

TRUE OR FALSE Writer Zane Grey was born in a town called Zanesville.

ANSWER True. Much of the lore of the West originated not in fact but in fiction. One of the most successful Western authors was Zane Grey, who was born in Zanesville, Ohio, in 1875.

> **★★★ FAST FACT ★★★**
>
> Robert LeRoy Parker and Harry Alonzo Longbaugh were known as Butch Cassidy and the Sundance Kid, the best-known members of the notorious Wild Bunch.

His books include *Riders of the Purple Sage*, *The Thundering Herd*, *Code of the West*, *West of the Pecos*, and *The Last of the Plainsmen*. Many of his stories were turned into movies.

Q. A stone monument is being carved in the Black Hills just 17 miles from Mount Rushmore. Who does this carving memorialize?

A. Courageous Lakota warrior Crazy Horse. The monument, which has been in progress since 1948, is planned to be 641 feet wide by 563 feet high. The head of Crazy Horse is 87 feet tall. By comparison, the heads of the four U.S. presidents at Mount Rushmore are each 60 feet tall.

Q. Who were Henry McCarty, William H. Bonney, William Antrim, and Kid Antrim?

A. All four names were aliases of Billy the Kid. The famed outlaw's real name was Henry McCarty, and the other names are just some of his many rumored aliases. After his death in 1881, legend proclaimed that he had killed 21 people, one for each year of his life. Interestingly, the famed Old West outlaw was born in New York City.

Q. Who led the Native American nations in the Battle of Little Bighorn, also known as "Custer's Last Stand"?

A. Sioux chief Sitting Bull, who once famously said, "We must stand together, or they will kill us separately." On

★★★ **FAST FACT** ★★★

The great Western novelist James Fenimore Cooper was raised in Cooperstown, New York, which was founded by his father.

June 25, 1876, General George Armstrong Custer's advance scouts reported an enormous Lakota and Cheyenne camp near the Little Bighorn River in Montana Territory. Disregarding his scouts' misgivings, Custer acted without waiting for the other two regiments that were on their way. Fatalities among the 7th Cavalry totaled more than 260, including Custer. Lakota and Cheyenne deaths were probably about half that.

TRUE OR FALSE Lincoln County sheriff Pat Garrett was hailed as a hero for killing Billy the Kid.

ANSWER False. Garrett, who relentlessly pursued the Kid and his gang across the county, had been charged with tracking down and arresting the outlaw, not killing him. When the lawman supposedly ambushed and killed The Kid in the middle of the night on July 14, 1881, his reputation was sullied. Garrett reportedly never received the $500 reward for Billy the Kid's capture.

"When I was young I walked all over this country, east and west, and saw no people other than the Apaches. After many summers I walked again and found another race of people had come to take it."
—Cochise, Apache chief

Q. Who was known as "the cowboy artist"?

A. Painter and sculptor Charles Russell, who brought the West to life in more than 2,000 paintings of cowboys, Native Americans, and landscapes set in the western United States.

Q. What future showman began the Civil War in the employ of the Pony Express and became a Union scout?

A. William Cody. After the war, his prowess as a buffalo hunter earned him a name, a reputation, and a subsequent career as the showman "Buffalo Bill." His "Wild West Show" helped establish many myths of the Old West.

TRUE OR FALSE Daniel Boone lost his life at the Alamo.

ANSWER False. Although it's often reported that Boone was one of the ill-fated soldiers who died defending the mission, in fact the pioneer and frontiersman died in 1820, 16 years before the Battle of the Alamo.

Q. Did Davy Crockett really kill a bear when he was three years old?

A. Maybe not, but Crockett swore it happened. Born in 1796, Davy Crockett was nearly a legend without fictitious additions to his story. What is true is that Crockett represented Tennessee in Congress, but when he was defeated for reelection, he went off to explore Texas. His travels led him into battle at the Alamo, where he was shot and killed.

Q. Which gunslinger is buried beside Wild Bill Hickok in Deadwood, South Dakota?

A. Calamity Jane. Martha Jane Canary roamed the West dressed as a man and toting a gun. She was an excellent shot and earned a reputation as being quite heroic and courageous. She may have been successful at shooting, but Calamity Jane was a calamity at marriage (she went to the altar 12 times) and at finances (she died penniless in 1903).

Bank robber and outlaw Charles "Pretty Boy" Floyd, who was celebrated as a 20th-century Robin Hood in a song by Woody Guthrie, so hated his nickname that he was known to have killed at least two people for using it. When he was shot down by federal agents in 1934, his dying words were "I'm Charles Arthur Floyd!"

Q. In 1883 it was discovered that an elusive criminal who robbed stagecoaches and mailboxes was actually a highly respected mining engineer named Charles E. Bolton. What was his outlaw name?

A. Black Bart. The infamous highwayman gained notoriety by leaving behind rhymes signed "Black Bart the Po8." His true identity was discovered when a laundry mark was found on a handkerchief dropped near the scene of a robbery.

★ Although lawman Wyatt Earp is remembered as a fast-shooting hero of the gunfight at the O.K. Corral and its violent aftermath (which earned him a reputation as the "toughest and deadliest gunman of his day"), the law officer in fact preferred the use of his fists over the use of firearms.

Q. Which member of the Dalton Gang survived the gun battle that killed his brothers, going on to a career in Hollywood?

A. Emmett Dalton. Emmett survived the 1892 raid in Coffeyville, Kansas, despite suffering 23 gunshot wounds. After spending 14 years in prison, he spent the rest of his life crusading against crime and for prison reform. He also made the most of his notoriety as an outlaw, earning a place for himself in Tinseltown as an actor and technical adviser.

TRUE OR FALSE Jim Bowie, one of the heroes who died at the Alamo, designed the bowie knife.

ANSWER False. Many people think "Big Jim" invented the bowie knife, but evidence shows that it was actually the design of his brother Rezin. The famed knife, with its 15-inch curved blade, was popularized because of its connection to the legendary Alamo fighter, who is said to have used it to cut down many Mexican soldiers during the raid.

Q. Which American artist gained fame with stirring paintings of the Old West—work that has become known as the best of the Western theme?

A. Frederic Remington. His work was based on his travels during the 1880s. Remington's Western sketches appeared in *Harper's Magazine.* He understood that the Wild West would soon be tamed, so he captured his images on canvas, such as *Cavalry Charge on the Western Plains,* and in bronze, like *Bronco Buster.*

Q. In 1900 a woman named Carry Nation did something for the first time. She would repeat this activity until her death in 1911, gaining national notoriety. What did Carry Nation do?

A. Smashed up a bar. After her first husband drank himself to death, Carry Nation went on a crusade. The Kansas woman smashed up her first barroom with bricks wrapped in newspaper but later became famous for wielding a metal hatchet. She attacked more than 20 saloons in the next year and was arrested more than 30 times. She paid her fines by selling souvenir hatchets. She called men "nicotine-soaked, beer-besmeared, whiskey-greased, red-eyed devils."

Tombstone Tale

★ ★ ★ ★ ★ ★ ★ ★ ★ ★ ★

Tombstone's most famous Boot Hill epitaph belongs to outlaw Lester Moore:

> Here lies
> Lester Moore
> Four slugs
> From a 44
> No Les
> No more

TRUE OR FALSE Johnny Appleseed was a real person.

ANSWER True. The real Johnny Appleseed was a man named John Chapman. Legend has it that during the first half of the 19th century, an eccentric but kindly man roamed the Western frontier—which at that time was Pennsylvania, Ohio, and Indiana—planting apple seeds. His beneficence was legendary, and, according to real-life accounts, Chapman was indeed a kind and generous man. As early as 1806, pioneers across the frontier had nicknamed Chapman "Johnny Appleseed."

Q. Who wrote *The Story of Bonnie & Clyde*?

A. Bonnie Parker herself. For a two-year period, 1932–34, Parker and Clyde Barrow captivated the nation by posing as that generation's Romeo and Juliet—on the lam from the law. The duo is credited with 13 murders and countless robberies, but many people think Clyde and his "Barrow Gang," not Parker, actually committed most of the crimes. Some in the gang claimed they never saw Parker fire a gun, despite the fact she was frequently photographed brandishing weapons. Parker helped immortalize their legend by writing *The Story of Bonnie & Clyde*, which she sent to the media.

Q. Which Texan quickdraw is said to have killed as many as 23 men by the time he was 18?

A. John Wesley Hardin. A rough and rowdy gambler, Hardin seemed to leave bodies in his wake wherever he went. Though he painted himself as a sort of "avenging angel" in his autobiography, he was quick to claim responsibility for numerous kills. By the end of his life, his death toll may have been as high as 50 or as low as 20, but either way, John Hardin was clearly one bloodthirsty gunslinger.

WORLD WAR II

★ ★ ★ ★ ★ ★ ★ ★ ★ ★ ★ ★

The greatest conflict of the 20th century spawned a colorful array of personalities in America—strong, independent, but all dedicated to the common cause of victory.

Q. Which entertainer traveled around the world performing for U.S. troops in wartime, beginning in 1941?

A. Bob Hope. Hope began entertaining troops during World War II and kept up the practice for the next 50 years, traveling wherever troops were stationed and inspiring other entertainers, such as The Andrews Sisters, to travel, too. In 1997 Congress made Hope an Honorary Veteran, a new title that had never before been bestowed.

"With confidence in our armed forces—with the unbounding determination of our people—we will gain the inevitable triumph—so help us God."
—President Franklin Delano Roosevelt,
December 8, 1941, Pearl Harbor speech

TRUE OR FALSE Navy pilot, and future U.S. president, George H. W. Bush was shot down over Iwo Jima.

ANSWER True. On September 24, 1944, Bush and two crewmen flew a bombing run over the Pacific. Their plane was hit by antiaircraft fire before it reached the target, but Bush continued. After releasing his payload, he bailed out over the Pacific, the only member of the crew to survive. He was later awarded the Distinguished Flying Cross.

Q. By what name was Iva Ikuko Toguri D'Aquino more commonly known?

A. Tokyo Rose. An American citizen with Japanese parents, she was visiting a sick relative in Japan when war broke out. She joined the Japanese Broadcasting Company and was trained by an American POW to broadcast Japanese propaganda in an appealing, cheery voice. In 1948 she was tried by the United States and sentenced to ten years in prison and fined $10,000 for treason.

Q. Which tough WWII general was a pentathlete in the 1912 Olympics?

A. General George S. Patton. Originally open only to military officers, the multi-event sport comprised pistol shooting from 25 meters, sword fencing, a 300-meter freestyle swim, an 800-meter horseback race, and a four-kilometer cross-country run. Patton placed fifth overall.

Q. Whose letter to Franklin D. Roosevelt in 1939 led to the development of the Manhattan Project?

A. Princeton professor Albert Einstein. Scientists sent FDR a letter that detailed the tremendous power released by the atomic process, as well as the enormous and deadly consequences. Einstein put his name to the letter, and Roosevelt approved the Manhattan Project, which brought together the efforts of more than 600,000 people to develop the atomic bomb. Einstein later had great regrets about signing the letter.

⭐ Prior to taking office in 1945 after President Roosevelt's death, Harry S. Truman knew absolutely nothing about the Manhattan Project or the atomic bomb. Roosevelt had kept word of the project top secret, and at the time of FDR's death Truman had only been his vice president for 83 days. This meant that Truman had only days to learn in detail what Roosevelt had been planning and studying for years.

"Had I known the Germans would not succeed in producing an atomic bomb, I never would have lifted a finger."

—Albert Einstein, expressing his regret on having helped create the atomic bomb

Q. He was World War II's most decorated soldier, and he went on to star in several big-budget movies. Who was this Congressional Medal of Honor winner?

A. Audie Murphy. A 1945 *Life* magazine cover featured Murphy as the most decorated GI of World War II. The 1955 film *To Hell and Back,* starring Murphy, was based on his best-selling autobiography.

Q. World War II sent many of America's young men overseas, leaving America's women to keep the country's business and industry running. What was their collective nickname?

A. Rosie the Riveter. Industries retooled their production for wartime products, and America's women stepped in where their husbands, brothers, and boyfriends had been—working shifts around the clock to support the country's war efforts.

★ Tens of thousands of American soldiers deserted their duty during World War II. Only one of these soldiers, Eddie Slovik of Detroit, was executed. Slovik, who had a criminal record for a series of petty thefts, turned himself in expecting to be jailed, but when military reviews turned up his criminal record, he lost his chance at clemency.

Q. In 1942, Calvin Graham, who served on the USS *South Dakota* during the Battle of Guadalcanal, won the Medal of Honor and the Bronze Star. The government later took these honors back. Why?

A. He was only 12 years old. Graham had lied about his age so he could fight in World War II, and when the truth came to light, he was dishonorably discharged. Later, his medals and honorable discharge were restored.

Q. Whose idea was it to use the Navajo language as a secret code against the Japanese?

A. Philip Johnston. Johnston was the son of a missionary to the Navajos and one of the very few non-Navajos who could speak their language fluently. The code ended up being completely undecipherable to the enemy and thus was a great success.

Q. Which major film icon not only enlisted to fight in World War II, but specifically requested to be put into combat zones?

A. James "Jimmy" Stewart. Stewart came from a military family and was eager to enlist when war broke out in 1941. Not wanting to be relegated to the sidelines, Stewart appealed to his superior and was assigned to the 445th Bombardment Group in 1943. His dedicated service saw him promoted to the rank of colonel before the war was over.

★ Pilot Richard "Dick" Bong proved himself to be a world-class flying ace by shattering the World War I record for most kills by a pilot, with 40 confirmed kills. The "Ace of Aces" was personally awarded the Medal of Honor by General Douglas MacArthur.

Q. Which Hollywood movie star invented a secret communications system to help the Allies in World War II?

A. Actress Hedy Lamarr, MGM's "It" girl in the 1930s and '40s. It turned out Lamarr was as smart as she was talented and gorgeous. She teamed up with inventor George Antheil to develop a method of manipulating radio frequencies that was nearly two decades ahead of its time. Although the Navy ultimately decided not to invest in their invention, Lamarr and Antheil had laid the groundwork for latter-day guidance systems. Today's cell phone technology and satellite communications use the frequency-switching system the pair invented in 1942.

> ★★★ **FAST FACT** ★★★
>
> Benjamin O. Davis was the first African American to rise to the rank of general in the U.S. armed forces.

★ Radio producer Norman Corwin initially brought the country together with his program *We Hold These Truths*, which was a celebration of the Bill of Rights that aired just after Pearl Harbor. It was so perfectly patriotic that in 1942 Corman was asked to produce another program to rally the American spirit. The 13-episode *This Is War* was broadcast around the world and served as an important piece of pro-American propaganda.

Q. How did U.S. Navy cook Doris "Dorie" Miller become the first African American to earn a Navy Cross?

A. Miller was responsible for rescuing many of his fellow soldiers during the attack on Pearl Harbor in 1941. He not only pulled many burned and drowning men from the water, he also took to an antiaircraft machine gun, where he bravely fired back at the attacking Japanese aircraft.

Q. Which Hollywood heavyweight's fascination with World War II history has helped earn him numerous Emmys, Golden Globes, and even several Academy Awards?

A. Steven Spielberg. Inspired by his father's war stories, Spielberg has tackled the subject in what seems like every way possible. His most notable works include the miniseries *Band of Brothers* and *The Pacific,* the Holocaust drama *Schindler's List,* and the epic *Saving Private Ryan,* which earned much praise for the realism of its battle scenes.

Hollywood Heroes
★ ★ ★ ★ ★ ★ ★ ★ ★ ★ ★ ★

World War II's call to arms attracted more than the everyday American; some well-known celebrities of the day served their country, too. A few of the most famous:

- Gene Autry (Air Force)
- Glenn Miller (Army Air Force Band)
- Clark Gable (Air Force)
- Elvis Presley (Army)
- John Ford (Navy photographic unit)
- Jimmy Stewart (Air Force)

TRUE OR FALSE The iconic image of Rosie the Riveter featured on the "We Can Do It!" posters was modeled after a real woman.

ANSWER True. The image was based on a photograph of factory-worker Geraldine Doyle. Like many women at the time, Doyle was working in a factory to help with the war effort. When a photographer sent to collect pictures of working women snapped a shot of her, she became history—although she wasn't even aware of the poster's existence until 1982.

Q. What dynamic news team can be credited with creating the lasting standard for live broadcast journalism during World War II?

A. Edward R. Murrow and William Shirer. When Murrow became the European director in London for CBS in 1937, he pitched his idea to do live news reports to seasoned reporter William Shirer. Together, the two brought a new dimension to radio newscasts. Their broadcasts brought the war home to inform the public as nothing else could.

Q. Which member of the "Buffalo Soldiers" single-handedly killed nine Germans; destroyed three machine-gun positions, an observation post, and a dugout; and led an advance patrol through a minefield, but was still passed over for the Medal of Honor?

A. Lieutenant Vernon Joseph Baker. Baker was awarded the Distinguished Service Cross, but after racial discrimination was discovered in the criteria for awarding medals, his Cross was upgraded. In 1997, President Bill Clinton awarded Baker the Medal of Honor he deserved.

Q. George, Francis, Joseph, Madison, and Albert Sullivan are responsible for an important piece of military legislature called the Sole Survivor Policy, but how?

A. The five brothers enlisted in the U.S. Navy and served together aboard the light cruiser USS *Juneau,* but their story turned tragic when the *Juneau* was sunk in November 1942, killing them all. The tragedy spurred the government to enact measures that would prevent family members from serving on the same ship or in the same unit, and to decree that, should there be a sole member still serving after the loss of two or more members of his family, he would be sent home. The story of the Sullivan brothers provided some of the inspiration for the film *Saving Private Ryan.*

A German shepherd named Chips served the 3rd Infantry Division in every major European and African operation of World War II. In appreciation of his loyal service, he was awarded the Distinguished Service Cross, Silver Star, and Purple Heart. However, the War Department later decided to save the medals for people, and all of Chip's awards were revoked.

Q. Who worked to make sure Japanese Americans received reparations for their unjust internment during World War II?

A. Alan Simpson and Norman Mineta. The two men met as boys when Simpson visited the Japanese internment camp Heart Mountain, where Mineta and his family were confined. As adults, Simpson became a U.S. senator and Mineta a U.S. representative, and together they succeeded in getting the U.S. government to issue a formal apology as well as more than $1.6 billion in reparations to Japanese Americans who had suffered, or had family members suffer, in American internment camps.

TRUE OR FALSE Major League Baseball star Bob Feller was drafted into service.

ANSWER False. "Bullet Bob" Feller was the sole provider for his mother at the start of the war, which meant there was no chance of him being drafted, but he signed up for the Navy the day after Pearl Harbor anyway. He became an antiaircraft gunner on the USS *Alabama* in 1942 and served in the treacherous North Atlantic before heading to the South Pacific Theater. He returned to baseball after the war, winning 26 games in his first full season back with the Cleveland Indians in 1946.

Q. Who was Mildred Fish-Harnack?

A. She was the only American woman to be executed at Hitler's order. A German-American teacher and translator, she fought against the Nazi regime by working as a spy for the U.S. military. Unfortunately, her act of bravery was discovered and she was guillotined at Plötzensee Prison in Berlin in 1943.

> ★★★ **FAST FACT** ★★★
>
> Joseph Rochefort cracked the Japanese Navy's JN25 code and intercepted plans for an assault on Midway Atoll, helping the Allies to a crucial victory.

"The best end for an old campaigner is a bullet at the last minute of the last battle."
—General George S. Patton